THE SILENCED ARMY

STUDY GUIDE

STUDY GUIDE

nichole chavez

Colorado Springs

Published by Equip Press, Colorado Springs, CO

First Edition: 2020
The Silenced Army Study Guide / Nichole Chavez
Paperback ISBN: 978-1-951304-09-6
eBook ISBN: 978-1-951304-10-2

A NOTE FROM NICHOLE

I BELIEVE WE, the Christian women of the world, are at a crossroads. We can choose to remain silent while the world cries out for the message of Jesus or we can stand up and volunteer to bring the Savior into our world.

For far too long we have been a silenced army, a sleeping giant. We have allowed the pressures of this world and sin to distract us and silence us from stepping into our purpose and calling. The world's message is strong, it is unified, and it has momentum. We have allowed our voice to fade into silence; we have been stuck in our pain and hurt for far too long. We have been a silenced army. But that is about to change!

In this ten-week book study that corresponds with *The Silenced Army*, you are given the tools to silence fear, pain, doubt, unforgiveness, shame, offense, pride, culture, and distraction. I don't like to cook, but I do cook at least five dinners a week because I've been told my family requires food to survive. One of the tools I have found that makes my dreaded nightly cooking session easier is this genius thing called a meal kit. All I have to do is choose how many meals I want a week and how many I'm making dinner for, and they will send me everything I need. In fact, they will have everything measured out and cut up for me, and on top of that they send step by step instructions so I know exactly how to put everything together to get the desired outcome of a tasty meal. Now I don't dread it so much, and my family can enjoy more than my three go-to meals week after week.

This study is a little like a meal kit. I have researched the scriptures, I give you instructions, I measured out your daily study time, but the rest is up to you. You have to put the ingredients together, you have to follow the step-by-step instructions, and you have to apply it to get the desired results - the God results.

There will be a temptation to quit while doing this study, the same temptation I had to quit while writing *The Silenced Army*. I wanted to quit when it got hard, or it touched a sore spot, or it required me to dig deep and be vulnerable. I'll be honest; there were a lot of tears in the writing of *The Silenced Army* and this study because I re-examined past wounds, I looked back at my selfish, hurting, broken and rebellious self and was forced to admit once again that I hurt my Savior. Then the joyful tears began to flow when I relived the moments

Jesus set me free, the moments when I started to silence fear, pain, doubt, unforgiveness, shame, offense, pride, culture and distraction. I began to use my voice to change the world for Jesus.

Whatever you do, don't quit; don't give up. Even if this study takes you 20 weeks instead of 10, don't give up. You were created on purpose and for a purpose; you were created to change the world for Jesus. In order to fulfill your purpose and calling you must go through the hard work of change, so together we can do the hard work of changing the world for Jesus.

I am on your side and in your corner cheering you on, my friend!

Love you,

— ***Nichole***
@nicholechavezministries
www.nicholechavez.com

CONTENTS

Week Five | Silenced By Shame

Week Six | Silenced By Offense

Week Seven | Silenced By Pride

Week Eight | Silenced By Culture

Week Nine | Silenced By Distraction

Week Ten | The Army

SILENCED BY FEAR

WEEK ONE | DAY ONE

We, the Christian women of this world, are a silenced army. Silenced by fear. The enemy has used fear to silence our army since the beginning of time. He uses our experiences—past and present—to stop us from showing up and speaking up.

He tells us that standing up for what God says is right will bring a firestorm of controversy, rejection, hurt, abandonment, isolation, and persecution.

He tells us that if we give in to God and step into our purpose we will be asked to do things out of our comfort zone, go places out of the safe zone, or put ourselves in the danger zone.

Has fear ever silenced you? Explain.

What did fear say would be the consequence of your obedience? Explain.

Do you feel it is safer to bow to fear than to stand up to it? Explain.

We are not victims of fear but rather volunteers. Fear feels like a safe emotion to listen to. We feel we should follow it to its conclusion because fear is a natural emotion to keep us safe in dangerous situations. The problem comes when we believe the lie that God has given us purpose and calling with the intent to harm us and that He is using our testimony and relationship with Him to hurt us. The enemy is sly; he uses the lifesaving emotion God created to silence us and bring us down to a bow.

Write down Psalm 23:4

Write down Psalm 34:4

Write down Deuteronomy 31:6

The enemy tricks us into thinking that God is the enemy and he is the reason we are to be fearful of our future our purpose and our calling. Instead, we learn from the above scriptures that God is on our side, he won't fail us or abandon us, he will protect us and he will strengthen us, he is fighting fear alongside us, not hurling fearful things at us. God never leaves us to face fear alone; he understands us, and the power fear has over us, so he battles along with us.

"For God has not given us a spirit of fear and timidity,
but of power, love, and self-discipline."
2 Timothy 1:7 NLT

Write down the three things God has GIVEN you in the scripture above.

1.
2.
3.

The Bible is full of stories about people who are put in impossible situations where they are forced to wait on God to save them, forced to make a decision for Christ before they know the outcome, forced to stand, even if they stand alone. These stories prove God's readiness to stand with us as we face what we most fear. Shadrach, Meshach, and Abednego are the perfect examples of this.

Read Daniel, Chapter three.
King Nebuchadnezzar decreed that everyone in his kingdom must bow down to the gold statue made in his image. If they didn't, they would be thrown into a fiery furnace and be burned to death. When the music sounded, everyone bowed accept three men: Shadrach, Meshach, and Abednego. They wouldn't bend their knees to the idol because they only bowed to God. I am sure they weren't the only three people who knew they shouldn't bow to the statue, but every person there bowed anyway out of fear. Their life was more important to them than standing out, standing up, and standing firm.

Fear silenced an army of people and brought them to a bow. Fear left only three people standing. Only three people decided that they would not be a part of the silenced army.

We respond to fear three different ways:

1. We run from it.
2. We bow to it.
3. We run to a solution.

Number two is my default programming. I bowed to the pressure of fear, I vowed to oppose God and His plan for my life in exchange for the safety of an ordinary life, a life of fighting my purpose, fighting God and the fear that one day I might give in and it might cost me everything I thought I needed and wanted. That's the real fear we all face. We think that if we give in to God and choose his way, his plan, and his path, we might lose everything we see as important. I certainly bought into the lie. I bowed.

Do you run, bow, or run to THE solution? Why? Explain.

"The name of the LORD is a strong fortress;
the godly run to him and are safe."
Proverbs 18:10 NLT

Shadrach, Meshach, and Abednego knew their decision to stand and not bow down to the statue would cost them their lives, and yet they chose to run to the solution, which is God. We tell ourselves that there are acceptable reasons for giving in to fear. God will understand that we are trying to preserve our way of life, God doesn't want me to be uncomfortable, or I don't want to get hurt. The lies we believe will end up shaping us, guiding us, and defining us.

Which lies do you believe? List them. Explain.

Do you believe these are reasonable excuses? Explain.

Shadrach, Meshach, and Abednego knew that fear was not an excuse for their bowing, and they refused to be silenced because they knew God. They knew he was not the enemy; they knew they wouldn't be alone; they knew that standing was the only option for those who truly trust God. They knew what God can do; they knew his power is infinite and has no limitations. Their intimate knowledge of God gave them the confidence, peace, and courage to not bow down to fear.

We are not to voluntarily be shaped, guided, or defined by fear. We are volunteers to trust in our God, silence fear, and stand up. Even if we stand alone.

"Don't be afraid, for I am with you.
Don't be discouraged, for I am your God.
I will strengthen you and help you.
I will hold you up with my victorious right hand."
Isaiah 41:10 NLT

Insert your name in the blanks and declare this over your life. Allow this scripture to replace your fear.

____________________ don't be afraid, for I am with you.

____________________ don't be discouraged, for I am your God.

I will strengthen ____________________ and help you.

I will hold ____________________ up with my victorious right hand.

SILENCED BY FEAR

Study - Reflect – Pray

WEEK ONE | DAY TWO

"For God has not given us a spirit of fear and timidity,
but of power, love, and self-discipline."
2 Timothy 1:7 NLT

Write a prayer admitting you have fears, and then tell God what your fears are.

Look up and write down a scripture that will encourage you to silence fear.

Look up and write down a scripture that will challenge you to fear less.

SILENCING FEAR

WEEK ONE | DAY THREE

We should not volunteer to be shaped, guided, or defined by fear. We are volunteers to trust in our God, silence fear, stand up. Even if we stand alone.

"Don't be afraid, for I am with you.
Don't be discouraged, for I am your God.
I will strengthen you and help you.
I will hold you up with my victorious right hand."
Isaiah 41:10 NLT

Insert your name in the blanks and declare this over your life.

____________________ don't be afraid, for I am with you.

____________________ don't be discouraged, for I am your God.

I will strengthen ____________________ and help you.

I will hold ____________________ up with my victorious right hand.

This scripture holds a promise. It says you will never be alone, cry alone, hurt alone, journey alone, stand alone, or go through the fire alone. It doesn't say you won't cry, hurt, journey or go through the fire. It doesn't promise to spare you from choosing faith and trust over fear. This is where we struggle. We want to be rescued before we go through the fire, we don't want to be forced to trust in God. We don't want to stand in the midst of a bowing crowd.

What would give you courage and boldness to stand when everyone around you is bowing? Explain.

There is safety in numbers; the silenced army is vast. You will never be singled out or made to stand alone. You will never be called upon to do something out of the ordinary, or be forced to stand when the rest of the world bows. You will never be asked to do anything except stay silent.

Silence is not merely silence. It's not harmless. The enemy uses your fear to silence you so all that is left to do is watch as the world turns against God, you silently observe the destruction of human life, you are forced to close your eyes and ears to suffering.

The silenced army may seem safe. It may feel comfortable, but it is an illusion. The fighting is happening, the losing army isn't just going home in defeat, the enemy is trying to annihilate us. Our opponent is out to kill, steal, and destroy. He is out for the eternity of everyone on this planet, and he is out for the souls of the people you and God love.

Do you believe God is with you even when you stand alone? Explain.

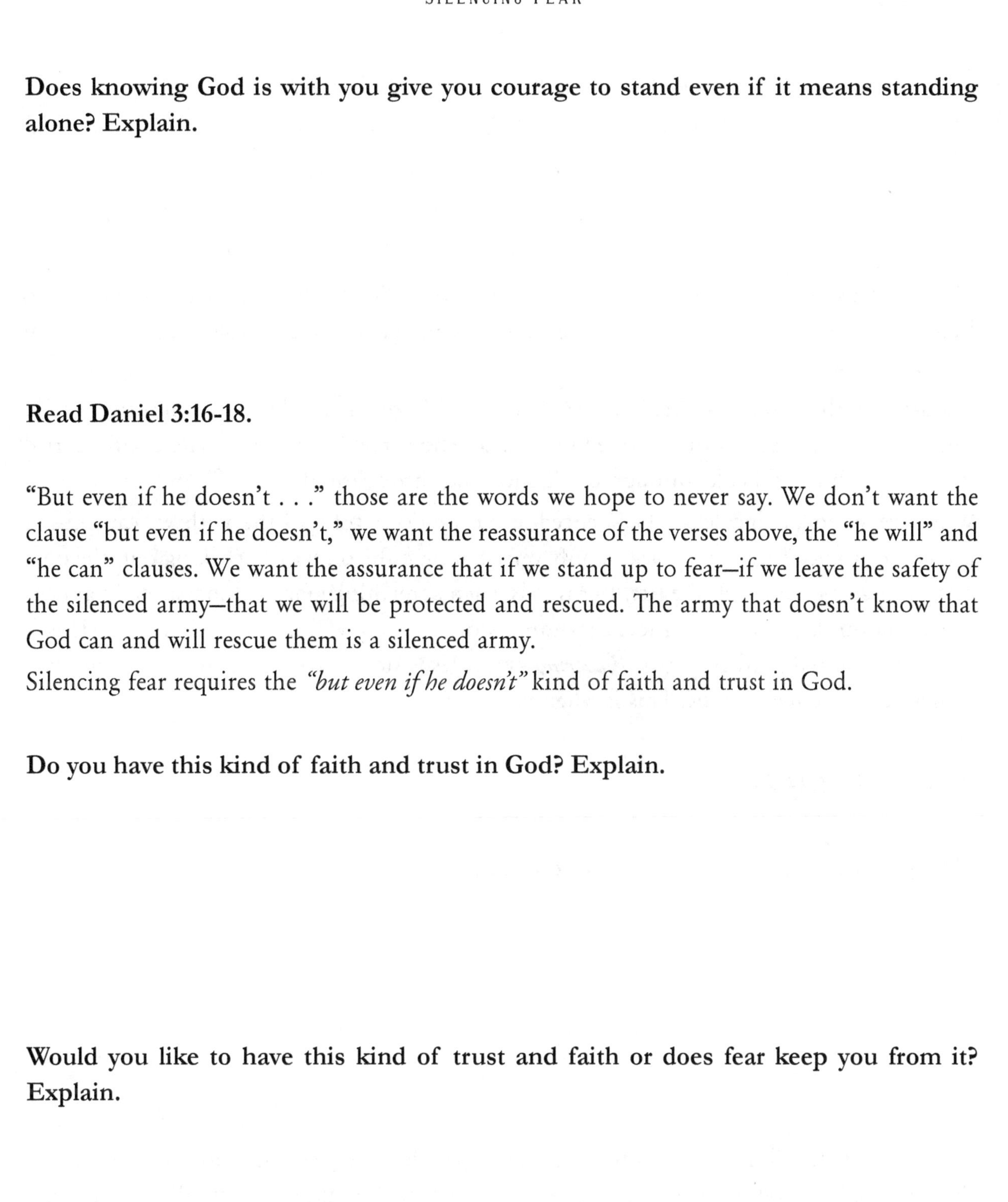

Does knowing God is with you give you courage to stand even if it means standing alone? Explain.

Read Daniel 3:16-18.

"But even if he doesn't . . ." those are the words we hope to never say. We don't want the clause "but even if he doesn't," we want the reassurance of the verses above, the "he will" and "he can" clauses. We want the assurance that if we stand up to fear–if we leave the safety of the silenced army–that we will be protected and rescued. The army that doesn't know that God can and will rescue them is a silenced army.

Silencing fear requires the *"but even if he doesn't"* kind of faith and trust in God.

Do you have this kind of faith and trust in God? Explain.

Would you like to have this kind of trust and faith or does fear keep you from it? Explain.

"Even though I walk through the darkest valley,
I will fear no evil, for you are with me;
your rod and your staff, they comfort me."
Psalm 23:4 NIV

This is a trust and faith verse, this is the kind of verse Shadrach, Meshach, and Abednego lived. This is the kind of verse that gives you the courage to stand in the midst of a fearful and bowing world.

The army of three, that was Shadrach, Meshach, and Abednego, did get thrown into the fiery furnace. A furnace so hot that it killed the guards who threw them into it. Their faith carried them through the ridicule, through the flames, and through it all.

When we stand up and leave the silenced army, we do it with all the faith we can muster up; we do it knowing we may be the only one standing, the only one speaking out, the only one willing to go through the fire. But this is when something amazing and special happens when you think you are going to be standing alone, but are willing to do it anyway. This is when the silenced army becomes *The Army*–when Jesus steps into the fire with you, and you realize you were never alone. This is when you see God.

Read Daniel 3:24-25.

How many people did Nebuchadnezzar see in the fire? Why?

When you silence fear and stand for your faith, people won't see you standing there alone, they will see Jesus too. They may not agree with you or with Jesus, but they will see him. They will know that he never lets us walk through the fire alone. He never leaves us or forsakes us, and he will never abandon us.

Silencing fear is a step of faith toward God, it's an acknowledgement of his love for you, and it means embracing trust in his promise to never leave you, abandon you or forget about you. It's a leap toward changing the world for Jesus. It's standing when the world bows.

"And I am convinced that nothing can ever separate us from God's love.
Neither death nor life, neither angels nor demons,
neither our fears for today nor our worries about tomorrow—
not even the powers of hell can separate us from God's love.
No power in the sky above or in the earth below—indeed,
nothing in all creation will ever be able to separate us from the love of God
that is revealed in Christ Jesus our Lord."
Romans 8:38-39 NLT

Insert your name in the blanks and declare this out loud.

I am convinced that nothing can ever separate _______________ from God's love.

Neither death nor life, neither angels nor demons, neither _________________ fears for today nor ________________ worries about tomorrow—not even the powers of hell can separate __________________ from God's love. No power in the sky above or in the earth below—indeed, nothing in all creation will ever be able to separate _______________ from the love of

God that is revealed in Christ Jesus our Lord."

SILENCING FEAR

Study - Reflect - Pray

WEEK ONE | DAY FOUR

"This is my command—be strong and courageous!
Do not be afraid or discouraged.
For the LORD your God is with you wherever you go."
Joshua 1:9 NLT

Write down the areas in your life that need you to stand instead of bowing.

Write a prayer asking God for courage to stand when the world around you bows.

Look up and write down a scripture that will encourage you to stand when you are tempted to bow or be silent.

SILENCED BY FEAR

No Longer

WEEK ONE | DAY FIVE

*"And **I am convinced** that nothing can ever separate us from God's love.*
Neither death nor life, neither angels nor demons,
neither our fears for today nor our worries about tomorrow—
not even the powers of hell can separate us from God's love.
No power in the sky above or in the earth below—indeed,
nothing in all creation will ever be able to separate us from the love of God
that is revealed in Christ Jesus our Lord."
Romans 8:38-39 NLT

Are you convinced that nothing can separate you from God's love?

Are you convinced that neither death nor life, angels nor demons can separate you from God's love?

Are you convinced that neither fears for today nor your worries about tomorrow can separate you from God's love?

Are you convinced not even the powers of hell can separate us from God's love?

Are you convinced that no power in the sky above or in the earth below—indeed, nothing in all creation will ever be able to separate us from the love of God?

We have to be fully convinced of these things to silence fear. You can't trust God and stand in the midst of a bowing world unless you are fully convinced of God's love for you. It is because of his love for us that we stand, it is because of God's love for this world that we silence fear and boldly stand up for Jesus and stand up to fear. It is because of God's love for the people in your life that you will silence fear and step into your purpose and calling, it is because of God's love that you share Jesus with your world.

I've learned that we are not victims of fear, we are volunteers.

Write your name in the blanks.

____________________ is not a victim of fear. __________________ is a volunteer.

You have fear, it doesn't have you. Acknowledging this is the first step towards fighting it. You have to know your God and also know your enemy. Your enemy is fear.

Say this out loud.

FEAR IS MY ENEMY. I NO LONGER HAVE FEAR. IT NO LONGER HAS ME.

Fear is a temptation, giving in to it is a choice. When you give in to fear you will feel trapped, you will feel like a slave, you will feel like the only way to silence it is to give into it, but those are all lies meant to silence you and the purpose and calling you were created to fulfill.

Have you ever felt trapped in fear? Explain.

I always thought that the fear I had was keeping me safe. I didn't know I was giving in to fear, I felt I needed fear, I felt safe with fear. I learned that my fear had nothing to do with me; it had everything to do with fear having the power over me, it wasn't a warm blanket, it was chains of bondage.

Fear does not protect us–it binds us, and holds us prisoner, it binds our purpose, calling and our voice. Fear causes us to doubt God and if we doubt God, we won't live for him, and if we don't live for him, we won't share him with a world that needs him, and if we don't share him the enemy wins.

If we want to change the world for Jesus, then we have to change. We have to see fear for what it is: the enemy's tactic to silence us. We have to trust that God will never leave us or abandon us. He will stand in the fire with us! God has gone beyond being with us, he has equipped us with power. Fear is not from God; he doesn't use it against us or on us. God has given us power, love, and self-discipline to silence fear.

"For God has not given us a spirit of fear and timidity,
but of power, love, and self-discipline."
2 Timothy 1:7 NLT

God has given you a spirit of power. He has equipped you with the tools to take fear captive, to silence it and to bring it to a bow at the feet of Jesus.

Declare this out loud. I AM EQUIPPED WITH GOD'S POWER TO SILENCE FEAR.

Are you ready to silence fear? List the fears you are ready to silence. Write down God's truths to these fears.

Write a prayer and scripture declaring fear as powerless in your life. Call your fears out by name and declare them silenced.

We are a volunteer army. We are women created by God on purpose and for a purpose. We were created to change the world around us for Jesus.

Changing the world for Jesus starts when you silence fear and stand up for your faith. Stand up when everyone bows, stand up even if you stand alone, stand up even if...

Shadrach, Meshach, and Abednego thought they stood alone while the silenced army bowed, but they were never alone–God was with them the entire time. They could have bowed. They could have given in to man's demands and threats but they chose to trust God instead.

"Fearing people is a dangerous trap, but trusting the LORD means safety."
Proverbs 29:25 NLT

Don't fear public opinion, the loudest voice, the harshest tone, the criticizing words, the threats, the insults, the opposing voice, or the pressure to keep silent.

When you choose to no longer be silenced by fear but instead choose to stand in the face of it, you are not alone. God is standing beside you. He stands next to you and says, "Now this is a girl I can change the world through."

______________________ is a girl God can change the world through!

SILENCED BY PAIN

WEEK TWO | DAY ONE

We, the Christian women of this world, are a silenced army. Silenced by pain.

The pain of loss.
The pain of rejection.
The pain of abuse.
The pain of betrayal.

Pain brings us down to a bow with the weight of it. Pain can feel eternal and will leave you feeling exhausted, hopeless, and broken–like pieces of your life are scattered, never to be recovered and restored.

Pain will lie to you. It will tell you you're weak and broken. Pain will tell you that your life is over, and you will never be the same. Pain will silence you. Pain will make you bitter, angry, and untrusting.

Have you ever experienced pain that brings you to your knees? Explain.

This is just what the enemy needs, an army silenced, your purpose, calling, actions and voice silenced by pain, unwilling to move or act, untrusting, and unable to stand.

In these moments of desperation, you may feel like running–but to where? There isn't a place on this earth that you can go where your pain won't follow you. There is one person you can go to anytime and anyplace you may be. He is a safe place a refuge a constant source of peace and healing. Jesus!

Jesus is the one place you can go where your pain has no power.

Read Mark 5:24-34.

In the scriptures you just read you met a lady who was in physical, mental, and emotional pain. She was desperate for her life to change; she was desperate for healing. She was desperate enough to do something unusual, against the rules, brave, desperate and faith-filled.

Her pain was her motivation to reach out to Jesus.

What did the lady do that was unusual and brave? Explain.

What did the lady do that was faith-filled? Explain.

God seems to take the brunt of our anger when it comes to pain. We want God to know where we stand with him, we want him to know that we think he failed us, we want him to know that we are mad at him. So, we either ignore him or we tell him how we feel about his lack of intervention in our pain. The lady we read about in Mark 5 could have blamed Jesus.

She could have been resentful of her current circumstances, but she didn't see him as the enemy but rather as her healer. She saw Jesus as her one chance at healing.

Do you believe your pain can be healed? Explain.

Do you believe that Jesus wants to heal you? Explain.

The enemy will try to convince you that you are alone in your pain and that no one will understand. He tells us our pain is unique to us, that this burden is ours alone to carry. He tells us that God doesn't care. We listen to the lies and we carry our pain as if it is part of us.

Then the enemy introduces shame; he tells us we deserve it, that we should be stronger, we shouldn't feel this much pain, we are weak, and the list of lies goes on, playing and re-playing in our minds. His tactics begin to work, as we believe the lie day after day.

We bow to pain instead of standing up to it; we bury the pain deep and live with the shame of it. No matter how deep you bury pain it will always rise to the surface.

Pain will taint everything it touches: marriages, family relationships, jobs, and your relationship with God.

Has pain in your life affected your relationships? Explain.

Has pain affected your relationship with God? Why?

Pain certainly affected my relationship with God, every time pain would rise to the surface, I would scold God. I had no one else to talk to so God had to hear it all. He got my complaints, anger, hurt, fear, bitterness, resentment, and shame. God is true to his word when he said "he works all things for good." (Romans 8:28). He took my rants and complaints as an open door to communication.

God can handle your complaints, anger, hurt, fear, bitterness, resentment, and shame. He will listen when you talk to Him. All you have to do is talk to him.

Again, I ask: Do you want your pain to be healed? Explain.

Are you ready to talk to Jesus about it? Explain.

Write down John 16:33.

What will you have while on this earth?

"Here on earth you will have many trials and sorrows" (NLT). This scripture says not only will we have trials and sorrows but we will have **many** trials and **many** sorrows. Like yours, my life is living proof of this scripture. I used to think that I had to carry each painful experience with me through life. I used to think that my pain was going to be a constant companion. I used to think that pain was exclusive to me. **Lies, all lies.** The enemy wants us to believe these lies, he wants us to silently bear the burden of our pain so we will remain silent about it. He knows if we believe God's truths instead of his lies then we will see that healing is a faith-filled moment away.

Pain, trials and sorrows are inevitable but you are not a victim to these. You are a volunteer to change it, you are a volunteer to reach for your healing, you are a volunteer to silence pain.

____________________ **is a volunteer to reach for my healing.**
Insert Name

____________________ **is a volunteer to silence pain.**
Insert Name

____________________ **is a volunteer to trust Jesus.**
Insert Name

SILENCED BY PAIN

Study - Reflect – Pray

WEEK TWO | DAY TWO

"He heals the brokenhearted and bandages their wounds."
Psalm 147:3 NLT

Write a prayer telling God about your pain.

Look up and write down a scripture that will encourage you to release your pain to God.

Look up and write down a scripture that will bring healing, peace and joy into your heart.

SILENCING PAIN

WEEK TWO | DAY THREE

"You keep track of all my sorrows. You have collected all my tears in your bottle.
You have recorded each one in your book."
Psalm 56:8 NLT

We know that pain, trials, and sorrows are inevitable but you are not a victim of these. You are a volunteer to change it, you are a volunteer to reach for your healing, and you are a volunteer to silence pain.

There is healing, there is peace, there is joy on the other side of pain and on the other side of your faith-filled pursuit of Jesus, he sees your internal suffering, he knows you are desperate for the pain to go away.

"Then Jesus said, 'Come to me,
all of you who are weary and carry heavy burdens,
and I will give you rest.'"
Matthew 11:28 NLT

Healing you is his priority. He sees your life and future. He sees the life you will have if you keep your pain. This life breaks his heart. It is filled with suffering, pain, loneliness, and heartbreak–a shattered and wasted life. He sees a silenced life.

He also sees the life you will have after you give your pain to him. He knows what will happen after you touch his robe. He sees healing, joy, freedom, purpose, confidence, and a life put back together by his masterful hands. He sees a life that will change the world–a life free of suffering.

Jesus doesn't see your pain when he looks at you. He sees your life without it.

Jesus doesn't see your brokenness when he looks at you. He sees your healed life.

Jesus doesn't see your hurt when he looks at you. He sees your life free of it.

Jesus doesn't see your weaknesses when he looks at you. He sees his strength in you.

In the verse above Jesus said, "Come to me." You can heal, you can live a life free from pain but you have to put aside anything and everything that keeps you from reaching out to Jesus. You have to go to him; you have to reach out to him. To be healed you need Him.

Read Mark 5:25-27

In Mark 5:27 what did the lady do to receive her healing?

The lady in Mark chapter 5 went to doctors and the scripture says she "suffered a great deal from many doctors" (NLT). She tried everything she knew how to do. She tried every human avenue. I can imagine she tried everything medically available, every natural herb, every wives-tale concoction, and every rumored cure. She was desperate, she was desperate for healing. Today, we are no different. We try to drown our pain, numb our pain, ignore our pain, and bury our pain. Pain is a symptom of something wrong, it is our body, heart and mind alerting us that if the cause of the pain is not dealt with there will be severe consequences. So why do we run from pain, why don't we run to Jesus with it?

What have you tired to numb or end the pain? Explain.

This unnamed woman, who was impoverished after spending all her money on a cure, had given up on hope. She was doomed to spend the remainder of her days in incredible pain from a condition that was getting worse by the day, condemned to spend the rest of her life isolated and plagued with rejection. She heard about Jesus and decided nothing was going to stop her from getting to him. Sickness, pain, rejection, hopelessness, loneliness, and desperation brought her to the crowd around Jesus.

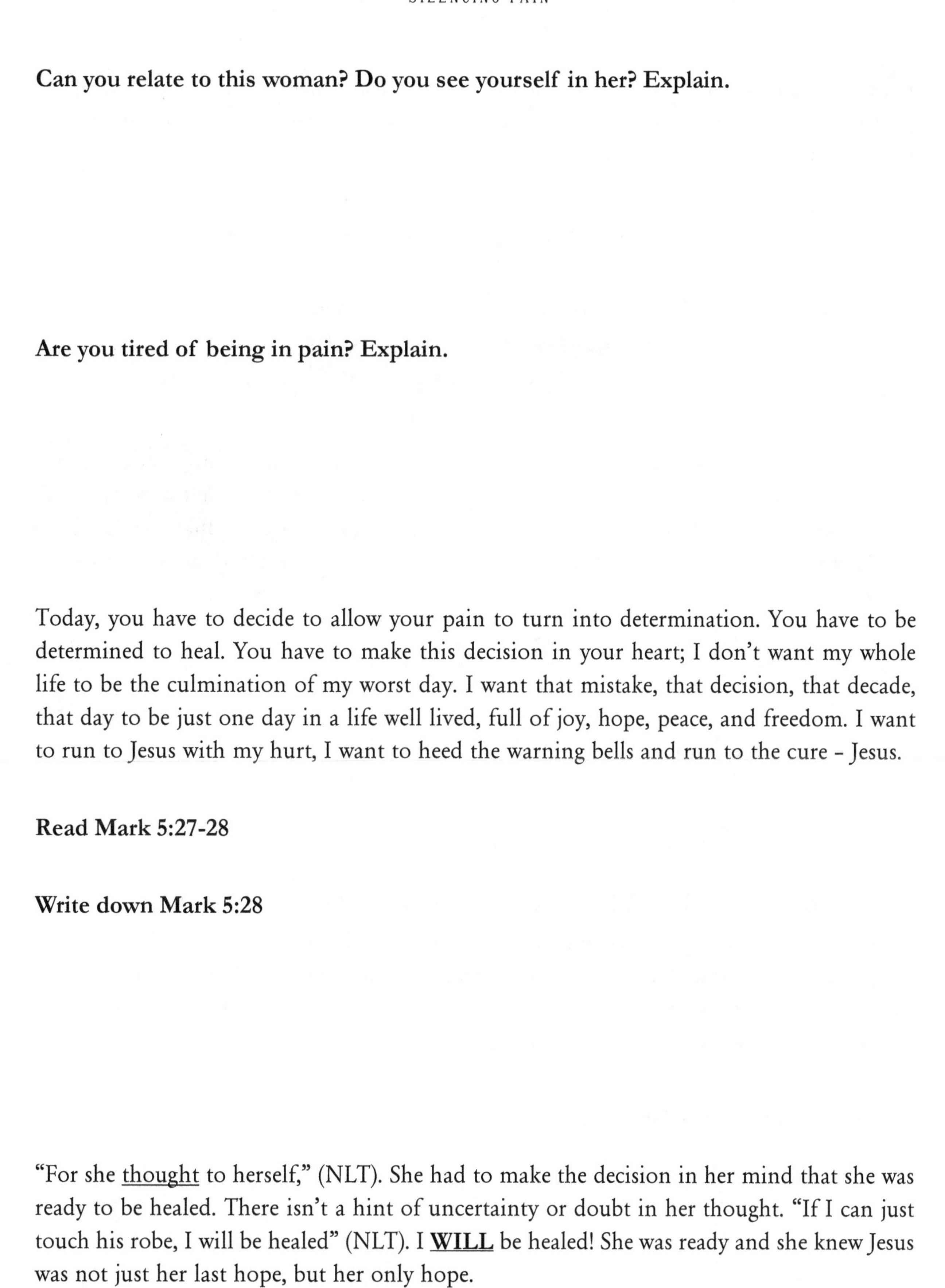

Can you relate to this woman? Do you see yourself in her? Explain.

Are you tired of being in pain? Explain.

Today, you have to decide to allow your pain to turn into determination. You have to be determined to heal. You have to make this decision in your heart; I don't want my whole life to be the culmination of my worst day. I want that mistake, that decision, that decade, that day to be just one day in a life well lived, full of joy, hope, peace, and freedom. I want to run to Jesus with my hurt, I want to heed the warning bells and run to the cure - Jesus.

Read Mark 5:27-28

Write down Mark 5:28

"For she thought to herself," (NLT). She had to make the decision in her mind that she was ready to be healed. There isn't a hint of uncertainty or doubt in her thought. "If I can just touch his robe, I will be healed" (NLT). I **WILL** be healed! She was ready and she knew Jesus was not just her last hope, but her only hope.

Jesus isn't your last hope; he is your only hope. He already made a way for you to receive your healing. He already paid the price and gave you access to healing at no cost to you. All you have to do is come to him with your pain and your faith.

"But he was pierced for our rebellion,
crushed for our sins.
He was beaten so we could be whole.
He was whipped so we could be healed."
Isaiah 53:5 NLT

Jesus took on indescribable pain so you wouldn't have to. He made healing available at the drop of a prayer and your faith in his healing power. The verse above isn't a story, it isn't an exaggeration; it is TRUTH. There is specific wording in this scripture that says "could be whole" and "could be healed," it says "could" because Jesus can do it but you have to believe he can?

Read Mark 5:29

Write down the first word in that verse?

"Immediately" she was healed. Not a week later, not a month later - IMMEDIATELY!

He's waiting for you to reach out and touch his robe. With faith stronger than your pain you tell yourself (as she did), "If I can just touch his robe, I will be healed." Then Jesus with love in his voice and in his eyes, allows healing to flow out of him and into you then he looks at you and says; "Go in peace. Your suffering is over."

Write down a prayer of faith and give your pain to Jesus.

SILENCING PAIN

Study - Reflect - Pray

WEEK TWO | DAY FOUR

"But he was pierced for our rebellion,
crushed for our sins.
He was beaten so we could be whole.
He was whipped so we could be healed."
Isaiah 53:5 NLT

1. Write your name in the blanks.

But he was pierced for ____________________ rebellion,

crushed for ___________________ sins.

He was beaten so _____________________ could be whole.

He was whipped so _____________________ could be healed.

2. **Write down your acknowledgment of pain and your declaration of healing. Let the enemy know that your God is bigger than your pain and he has lost the battle to use pain to silence you.**

3. **Look up and write down scriptures that speak healing into your life, heart, body and soul.**

SILENCED BY PAIN

No Longer

WEEK TWO | DAY FIVE

"Heal me, LORD,
and I will be healed; save me and I will be saved,
for you are the one I praise."
Jeremiah 17:14 NIV

Jesus can see that the healing you experience on the other side of pain will become more than your story, it becomes your testimony. By standing up to pain and reaching for your healing, you become a walking and talking beacon of hope, a living and breathing symbol of healing, a banner for freedom, and an example of healing. You can be more than changed by healing you can change the world for Jesus with your powerful story of God's healing, and your submission and willingness to exchange your pain for peace, joy, and freedom.

Your life now becomes proof of this verse: Romans 8:28 (write it below).

Your deepest hurt, your greatest suffering, your crippling pain can be used by God to change the world. The enemy, who hopes to silence you with pain, is now defeated.

An army standing tall, unafraid, unmoved, confident, and expectant that through our story of healed pain, others will come to find the same hope and healing. By our example of reaching out for the robe of Jesus, you will give others the courage to do the same.

This is how we change the world for Jesus. We lead by example, by walking in freedom and healing, and we tell everyone who will listen. We don't bow to pain, we stand in the face of it–healed, made whole, and suffering no longer.

Read Revelation 12:10-11. Write down verse 11.

We, the Christian women of the world, are no longer silent. We are ready to share the healing power of Jesus with anyone in pain or who is suffering, bullied, rejected, depressed, abused, trafficked, enslaved, addicted, raped, and silenced in our world. We will defeat the enemy, by the blood of the Lamb and by our testimony. Our testimony, our story of healing is a weapon to be used against the enemy.

Write down 1 Peter 3:15.

"...And if someone asks about your hope as a believer, always be ready to explain it." (NLT) Our mandate is to be ready when we are given the opportunity to share what Jesus has healed us from, freed us from and redeemed us from. We are to be prepared at all times without any hesitation.

Are you prepared to share your story? Explain.

The world is full of hurt and pain, it longs for healing, it searches for the cure. The world continually finds pain and hurt because as long as there is sin, atrocities will continue to happen. Pain will be inevitable, but as long as one person is willing to stand up, there will always be Jesus. You are not alone in sharing your story of healing and hope, there are millions of ladies around the world who are sharing their story every day, together we are able to share the power of Jesus around the world with the same determination and courage that the woman who touched Jesus' robe had.

We are not powerless in this world, we are empowered. We will not bow, we will stand. We are not silenced, we are speaking out. We are not broken, we are healed. We are not alone, we have Jesus.

List the reasons that keep you from sharing your story of God's healing with others? Explain.

Every single one of those reasons you listed above has a solution. Find them. Write each reason you listed on a separate 3x5 card and start finding solutions for them one by one. Write the solution on the back and put it into practice.

If the enemy can't silence you with pain, he will gladly take any silence at all. Let's read that again. <u>If the enemy can't silence you with pain, he will gladly take any silence at all.</u>

Keeping your healing to yourself is just as damaging to the world around you as not being healed at all. Your healing is for you and all who will be brave enough to reach for Jesus' robe because you had the boldness and courage to share your healing.

"Sing to the LORD; praise his name.
Each day proclaim the good news that he saves.
Publish his glorious deeds among the nations.
Tell everyone about the amazing things he does."
Psalm 96:2-3 NLT

Each day we are supposed to "proclaim the good news that he saves. Publish his glorious deeds among the nations." So how do we practically prepare to do this? There are countless ways but I will list three for you.

1. Ask God to bring the people who need to hear your story of healing to you or you to them.
2. Be prepared to tell your story of healing in three minutes or less. Your story will start with the problem/hurt and end with the solution/healing.
   Example: I was hurt... I was fed up/ at the end of myself/ broken/ tired/ etc. I took my hurt to Jesus/ I prayed/ I went to church and heard about Jesus/ etc.... He healed me/ set me free/ restored me/ etc.
3. Love your story of healing. I thank God almost every day for the healing I have received, I view it as a gift and because of that I have no problem telling anyone who will listen. When God heals you it becomes less about telling your story and more about telling God's story of healing you.

Here's your assignment. You can write it here or you can write it on a separate piece of paper so you can read it every day.

Write a prayer asking God to send the person/people who need to hear your story of healing to you or you to them.

Write your story of healing below.

Write a prayer of thanking God for all he has healed you from.

When you choose to no longer be silenced by pain, but instead choose to stand in the face of it, you are not alone. God is standing right beside you. He stands next to you and says, "Now this is a girl I can change the world through."

______________________ is a girl God can change the world through!

SILENCED BY DOUBT

WEEK THREE | DAY ONE

We the Christian women of this world are a silenced army. Silenced by doubt.

Doubtful that we can make a difference.
Doubtful that we are enough.
Doubtful of our worth.
Doubtful of our purpose.
Doubtful of God's love.
Doubtful that God will do what he says he will do.

List your doubts below.

Doubt is the thief of trust, hope, and faith. It will leave you feeling guarded and alone. It will force you to put distance and mistrust between you and God.

Do you currently (or have you ever) doubted God? Explain.

In my experience doubt is worse than fear. Fear is for ourselves, we use it to protect ourselves; we use it to keep us safe. Fear is a selfish emotion. Doubt is a direct insult to God, it is saying, "I don't trust you," or maybe, "I don't fully trust you." It is a direct attack on the character of God. When we doubt him, we are telling him that whatever his plan, whatever his path, whatever his purpose is for us, it isn't good enough. We unwittingly say, "God, I know better than you, my way can be trusted, I choose myself over you, and I choose any advice over yours." James 1:6 (NIV) puts it this way; *"the one who doubts is like a wave of the sea, blown and tossed by the wind."* Doubt leaves you at the mercy of today's feelings. It anchors you to your emotions instead of to God who has the solutions. When you are anchored to your emotions you are anchored to the problem.

Do you or have you ever doubted yourself? Explain.

If you are anything like me you answered "yes" to the previous two questions. Yes, I doubt God and yes, I doubt myself and I absolutely don't believe, rely on or trust the enemy, so who is left to trust? How can we doubt everyone we trust and expect to be changed and change the world for Jesus? We have to put our trust somewhere: we have to anchor our emotion in Jesus. We must trust him.

Write down Psalm 37:5

There are three easy steps in the verse above. Write them below.

1.

2.

3.

"Commit everything you do to the LORD. Trust him, and he will help you."
Psalm 37:5 NLT

God has an answer for every question, a solution to every problem, healing for every sickness, mending for every brokenness, direction for the lost, guidance for the misdirected and he is the light that will dispel the darkness in your life. God can be trusted, he can be relied on and he can be counted on to never leave you or abandon you. If we doubt God, we will never do anything for him. Why would we? If we don't trust him then we don't trust what he says and if we don't trust what he says then why would we tell anybody else to trust him. The short answer is: we won't.

Has your doubt in God stopped you from doing what he has asked you to do? Explain.

An army that doubts its leader is a silenced army.

We can't win without trust in our commander and leader. We are supposed to be an army united by God, himself. We are supposed to be an army with the common goal of sharing Jesus with the world. We are supposed to be an army who wants the next generation to carry the message of Jesus forward. We are supposed to be an army that wants to stop and drown out the voice of the enemy with the message and righteousness of Jesus. We are supposed to trust our God wholeheartedly.

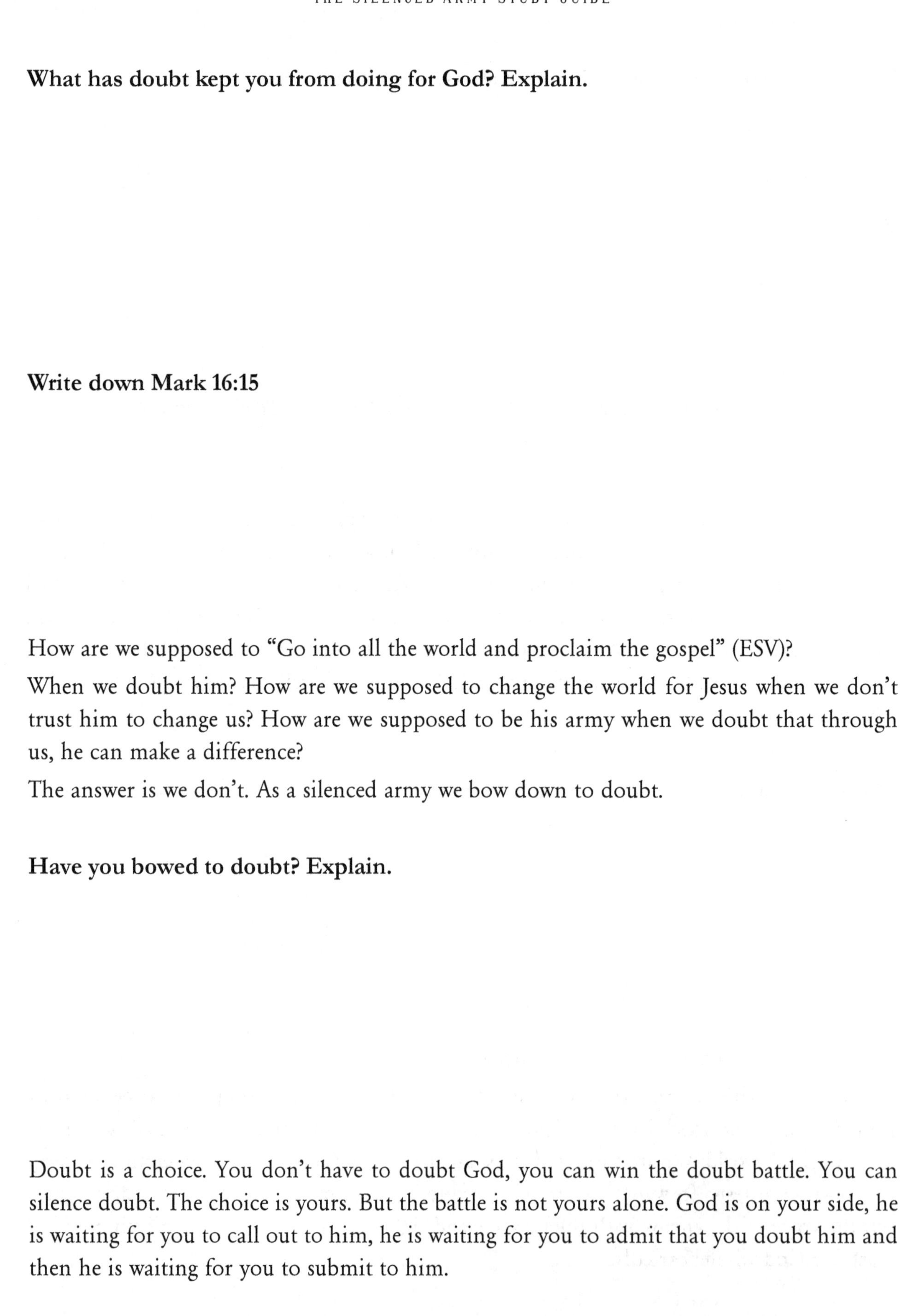

What has doubt kept you from doing for God? Explain.

Write down Mark 16:15

How are we supposed to "Go into all the world and proclaim the gospel" (ESV)?

When we doubt him? How are we supposed to change the world for Jesus when we don't trust him to change us? How are we supposed to be his army when we doubt that through us, he can make a difference?

The answer is we don't. As a silenced army we bow down to doubt.

Have you bowed to doubt? Explain.

Doubt is a choice. You don't have to doubt God, you can win the doubt battle. You can silence doubt. The choice is yours. But the battle is not yours alone. God is on your side, he is waiting for you to call out to him, he is waiting for you to admit that you doubt him and then he is waiting for you to submit to him.

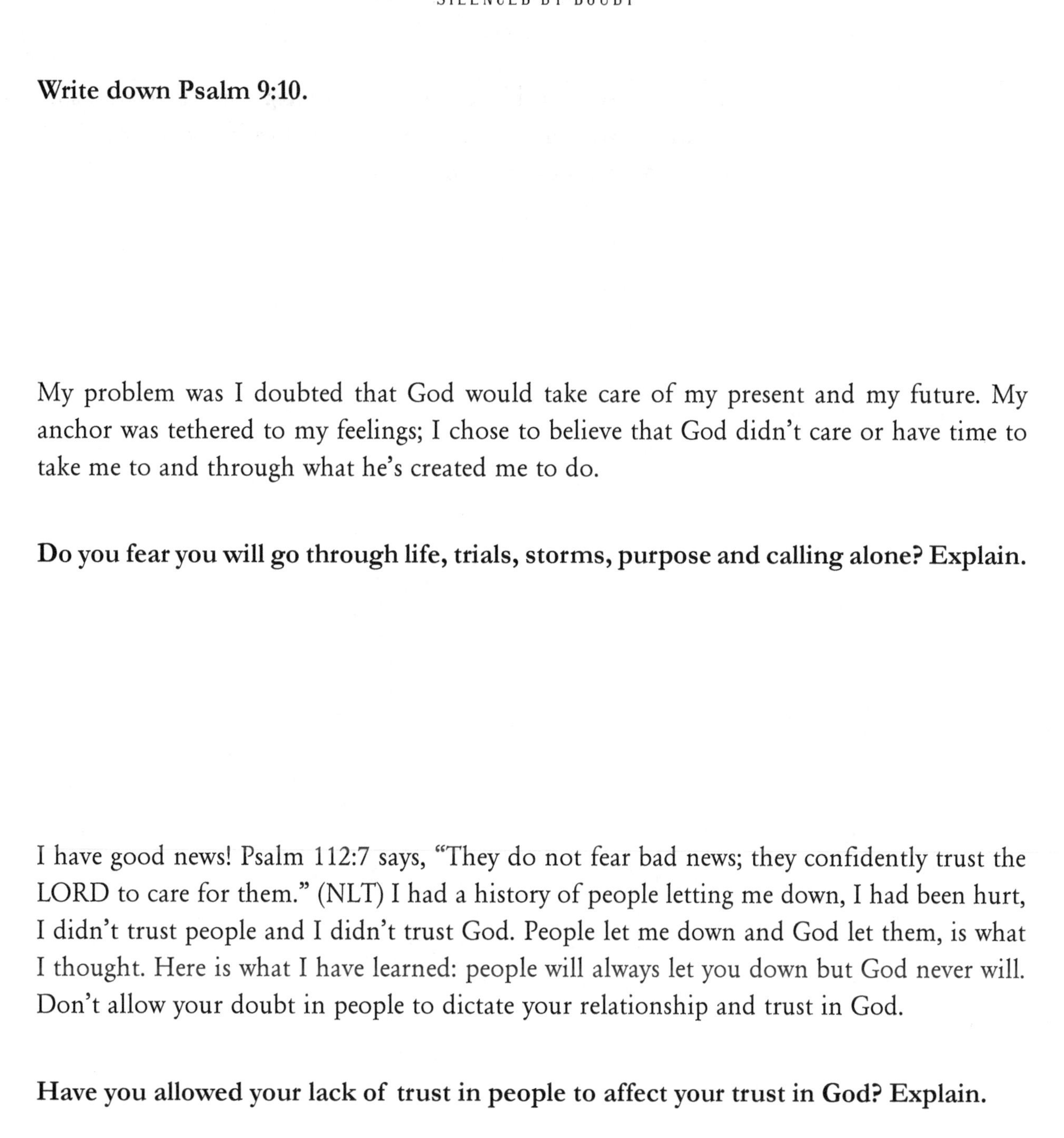

Write down Psalm 9:10.

My problem was I doubted that God would take care of my present and my future. My anchor was tethered to my feelings; I chose to believe that God didn't care or have time to take me to and through what he's created me to do.

Do you fear you will go through life, trials, storms, purpose and calling alone? Explain.

I have good news! Psalm 112:7 says, "They do not fear bad news; they confidently trust the LORD to care for them." (NLT) I had a history of people letting me down, I had been hurt, I didn't trust people and I didn't trust God. People let me down and God let them, is what I thought. Here is what I have learned: people will always let you down but God never will. Don't allow your doubt in people to dictate your relationship and trust in God.

Have you allowed your lack of trust in people to affect your trust in God? Explain.

God will take care of you, he is consistent in his love for you, strategic in his relationship with you, persistent in his perusal of you, and he is faithful in his love for you. You don't have to fear the future because God promises to be there, too.

SILENCED BY DOUBT

Study - Reflect - Pray

WEEK THREE | DAY TWO

"Commit everything you do to the LORD. Trust him, and he will help you."
Psalm 37:5 NLT

1. Write a prayer telling God about your doubt in him and his plan for your life.

2. **Write a prayer telling God about your mistrust in people.**

3. **Look up and write down scriptures that will encourage you to trust God with everything in your life.**

1.

2.

3.

SILENCING DOUBT

WEEK THREE | DAY THREE

Together we have learned that you can trust God with your life, heart, present life, and future but it is easy to doubt God when you feel like you are one in 8 billion.

Do you feel unseen or unheard by God? Explain.

To God, you are ONE, his one and only. He remains with you at all times; when things are good, bad, hard, happy, sad, disappointing, heartbreaking, exciting, joyful, victorious. He will stay when others leave. He will be there when you are alone in your hurt. He will be there when you feel like you can't go on. He is there even when you doubt him. He is there when you are doubtful that you can make a difference, doubtful that you are enough, doubtful of your worth, doubtful of your purpose, doubtful of God's love for you, and doubtful that his plans for you are good.

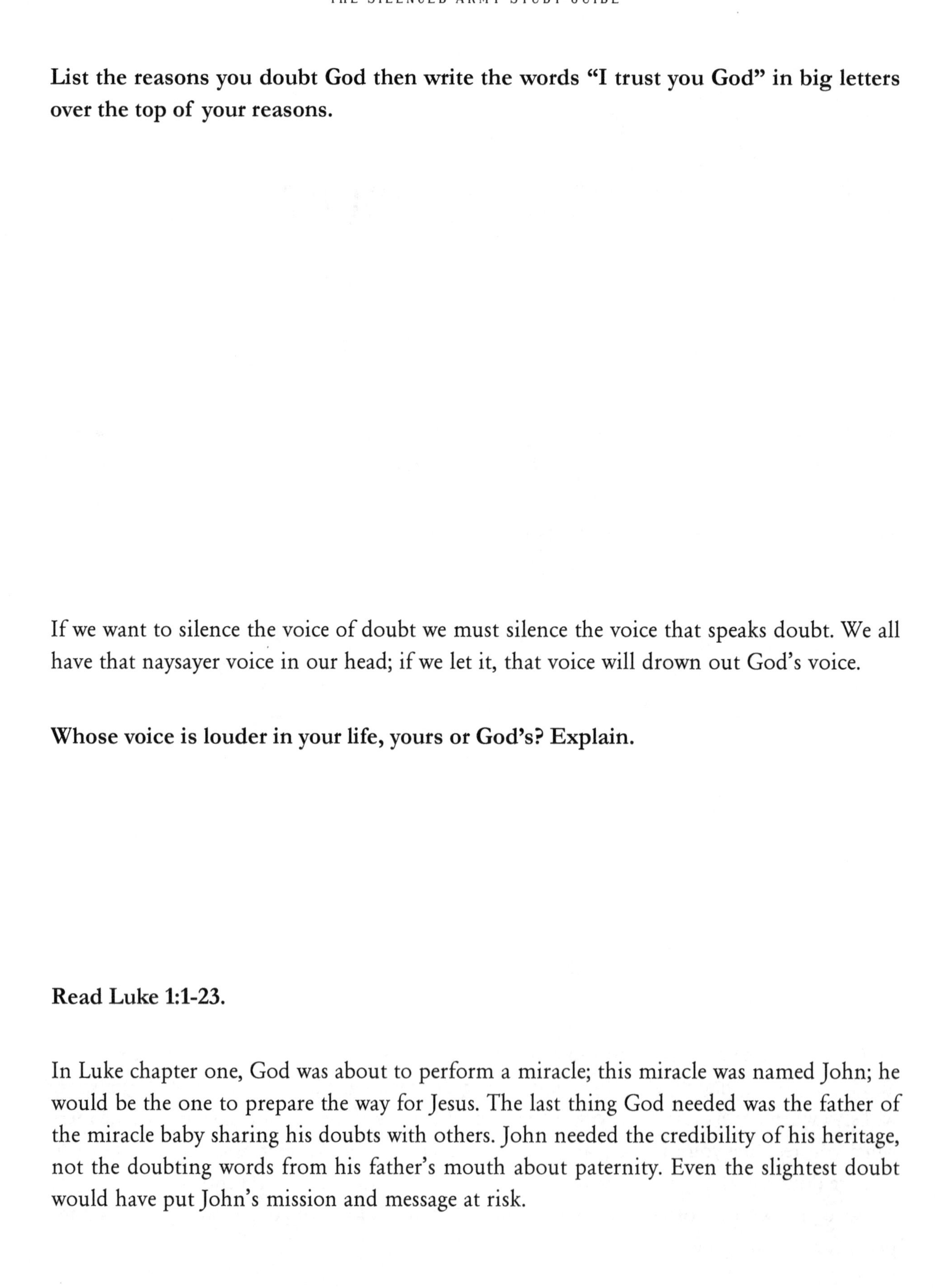

List the reasons you doubt God then write the words "I trust you God" in big letters over the top of your reasons.

If we want to silence the voice of doubt we must silence the voice that speaks doubt. We all have that naysayer voice in our head; if we let it, that voice will drown out God's voice.

Whose voice is louder in your life, yours or God's? Explain.

Read Luke 1:1-23.

In Luke chapter one, God was about to perform a miracle; this miracle was named John; he would be the one to prepare the way for Jesus. The last thing God needed was the father of the miracle baby sharing his doubts with others. John needed the credibility of his heritage, not the doubting words from his father's mouth about paternity. Even the slightest doubt would have put John's mission and message at risk.

In Luke 1:1-23 who doubted God and who trusted God?

Were their circumstances different?

Were their age and lifestyle different?

In your opinion why do you think Elizabeth trusted God and Zachariah doubted God?

As a result of Zachariah's lack of trust what did he loose?

Elizabeth chose to silence doubt. Elizabeth got to keep her voice. She was trusted to speak because she believed, and she gave the Lord credit. She declared, "The Lord has done this for me." She didn't just silence the voice of doubt–she didn't have any doubt, and she used her voice to declare trust. She lived an entire life waiting and trusting God, even though she felt disappointment month after barren month. According to human standards, she had every reason to doubt God, but she didn't. Instead, she silenced doubt and embraced trust–month after month, year after year, and decade after decade. She silenced doubt until the day she held her newborn promise–her son.

Read Luke 1:29-45.

Write down Luke 1:45.

I believe Elizabeth said those words out of experience. She believed, trusted and waited on God to fulfill his promise and when the time came she was able to not only enjoy it but also share it.

You may be part of the silenced army because you are struggling with trust. You know that you doubt God, but you can't bring yourself to trust him, so instead of being silenced by God you have silenced yourself. You withhold your story of healing, redemption, forgiveness and restoration because you are in a period of mistrust or doubt because your prayers haven't been answered or maybe he answered it *his* way instead of yours.

You are not alone; your doubts are not a disqualifier; your struggle does not mean failure in fact God is pleased when you wrestle with silencing doubt. Your struggle is a motivator for God to bring you to the place of trust. Don't fight the process, don't see the pain of the process as a false reminder that God can't be trusted, but rather as a reason to silence the voice of doubt and chose to trust God.

Write down the two things you are asked to do in Proverbs 3:5.

1.

2.

The message here is simple and empowering, it gives us a clear roadmap to freedom from doubt. We are to trust him because he knows better than we do, he knows what the future holds and he knows how to lead us to his plan for our lives. The life he has planned for you is found in Jeremiah:

"'For I know the plans I have for you,' says the LORD.
'They are plans for good and not for disaster,
to give you a future and a hope.'"
Jeremiah 29:11 NLT

The enemy wants you to live in doubt because if he can keep you doubting God, he can stop you from trusting everything God says about you and to you. He can prevent you from fulfilling your purpose, he can keep you locked in the army silenced by doubt. He can stop you from changing the world for Jesus.

Your purpose is important but not more important than the mission, the mission is to change the world for Jesus, that mission can't have doubting voices coming from the army which is supposed to deliver the message.

You are not a victim of this sinful world: You are a volunteer to change it. You are not silenced by doubt: You are the silencer of doubt.

Write your declaration of trust in God and your resolve to silence doubt.

SILENCING DOUBT

Study - Reflect - Pray

WEEK THREE | DAY FOUR

Fill in the blanks with your name

____________________trust in the LORD with all your heart;

____________________do not depend on your own understanding.

____________________seek his will in all you do,

and he will show _________________ which path to take.
Proverbs 3:5-6 NLT

1. **Write down Psalm 56:3**

2. Write down Psalm 84:12

3. Write down Proverbs 3:5-6

4. Write down Isaiah 26:3

5. Write down John 14:1

SILENCED BY DOUBT

No Longer

WEEK THREE | DAY FIVE

Together we are an army that silences the voice of doubt, we will unapologetically, boldly and confidently share the saving message of Jesus. This message will replace lies with truth, bring hope to the hopeless, healing to the sick and broken, joy to the depressed, peace to the anxious, direction to the lost, significance to the unseen, a hearing ear to the unheard, freedom to the enslaved, and Heaven to the Hell-bound. The voice that will be heard is the voice that trusts their Leader, believes in the message and silences the voice of doubt. **You are that voice.**

You are no longer a victim of doubt: you are a volunteer to silence it.

______________________ **is not a victim of doubt.**

______________________ **is a volunteer to silence it.**

If we, the united army of God, want to change the world for Jesus, we must not become victims of doubt, but volunteers to change the world and silence doubt. We must recognize doubt for what it is: a direct insult to God. Doubt says, "I don't trust you," or maybe, "I don't fully trust you." It is an attack on the character of God. When we doubt him, we are telling him that whatever his plan is, wherever his path leads, whatever his purpose, it isn't good enough. We have to be wise to the enemy's tactics and we must be prepared to combat his lies and deception.

We know God can be trusted, he will guide us and lead us beside still waters, he will protect us and our calling and purpose, he will light our path, and will love us unconditionally and eternally.

Write a prayer to God, tell him that you trust him, tell him you are going to silence doubt and give voice to trust.

"But blessed are those who trust in the LORD
and have made the LORD their hope and confidence.
They are like trees planted along a riverbank,
with roots that reach deep into the water.
Such trees are not bothered by the heat
or worried by long months of drought.
Their leaves stay green,
and they never stop producing fruit."
Jeremiah 17:7-8 NLT

As we previously read in Luke chapter one, Elizabeth lived an entire life waiting and trusting God, she was like a tree planted by the riverbank, she had roots reaching deep into the water. According to human standards she had every reason to doubt God, but she didn't doubt God or allow her worry to have a voice in her life, in her heart, or in her head. She wasn't pressured to bow or to doubt. Instead, she gave voice to trust and belief.

As a result, she was the first to congratulate Mary and encourage her with the powerful words in Luke 1:45 (NLT) "You are blessed because you believed that the Lord would do what he said." What was stored in Elizabeth's heart, what she lived and practiced in her life came out of her when she saw Mary. When you speak to people or when your faith collides with your world you will reveal trust in God or your lack of it. What is in your heart will come out of your mouth and will be displayed through your life. You can change the world for Jesus with one decision to trust God.

God doesn't deserve your doubt. He deserves blind trust; complete faith and he deserves to have an army that silences doubt. He deserves an army that is willing to stand when everyone else bows, and is willing to change the world for him.

Do you want your faith in God or your doubt in God to be displayed through your life? Explain.

It is time to declare:

I trust you, God.

Through Christ, I can make a difference.

With Christ, I am enough.

Because of Christ, I am worthy.

I was created on purpose and with a purpose.

I am loved by God.

I was created to change the world for Jesus.

Write the above statements in the numbered slots below. In place of "I" write your name.

1.

2.

3.

4.

5.

6.

7.

Have you ever known people who seem abnormally confident in who they are in Christ? They know scripture, they pray beautiful and powerful prayers, and they give sound advice that is full of wisdom. I've known people like this and my first thought used to be, "they must be super spiritual" or, "they must spend every waking minute studying their Bible and praying." This made my relationship with God seem shallow in comparison and a better relationship seem unattainable.

When you meet these people you are seeing the result of trust in God, you are looking at those who have silenced doubt and believed that God will do (and is doing) all he said he would do. You can be one of these people, a woman of God who trusts him, believes him, is willing to display your faith in him and determined to silence doubt. You are his chosen daughter, you are not alone, we are an army we are united in our mission to change the world for Jesus - silent no longer!

What would change in your life if you silenced doubt and started trusting God? Explain.

What do you need to change in your life to silence doubt? Explain.

Whatever you wrote above, start doing it today. Don't delay. The time is now, the army needs you and your purpose, calling and voice.

When you choose to no longer be silenced by doubt and instead choose to stand in the face of it, you are not alone. God is standing right beside you. He stands there next to you and says, "Now this is a girl I can change the world through."

______________________ is a girl God can change the world through!

SILENCED BY UNFORGIVENESS

WEEK FOUR | DAY ONE

We, the Christian women of this world, are a silenced army: silenced by unforgiveness. Unforgiveness is a slow acting poison in your heart, soul, life, calling, and purpose.

Are there people (or even one person) you need to forgive? Name them.

Unforgiveness will slowly destroy your peace of mind, your health, your relationships, your trust in God, your reliance on faith, and your hope in Jesus.

What has unforgiveness destroyed in your life? Explain.

I understand the struggle to forgive, I understand the feelings and justifications we think we have. To this day, forgiving those who have hurt me has been the hardest thing I have ever done. I didn't want to forgive; I didn't want to pray for my enemy, I didn't want anyone who had hurt me to enjoy the gift of forgiveness when they never asked for it.

What reasons do you have that justify unforgiveness? Explain.

I would like to say that the enemy had trapped me in unforgiveness, but that would be a lie. I hung on to it because I didn't want to let it go. I liked that anger and unforgiveness made me feel guarded, it gave me courage to look them in the eye when in the past I would have cowered. I liked that it gave me an excuse to be unkind and mean.

I felt justified. I felt empowered. I felt strong. I liked unforgiveness. It felt good.

Has unforgiveness given you false courage? Explain.

We feel justified. We feel empowered. We feel strong. We like unforgiveness. It feels good. But only for a while. Eventually these feelings start to bring us down to a bow; we are no longer in control of these feelings, they now control us. Unforgiveness is keeping us tethered to the past, it blinds us to our future and the purpose God has for us. Unforgiveness will trap us in a maze of memories, it binds us with shackles of emotions and keeps us from giving or accepting forgiveness.

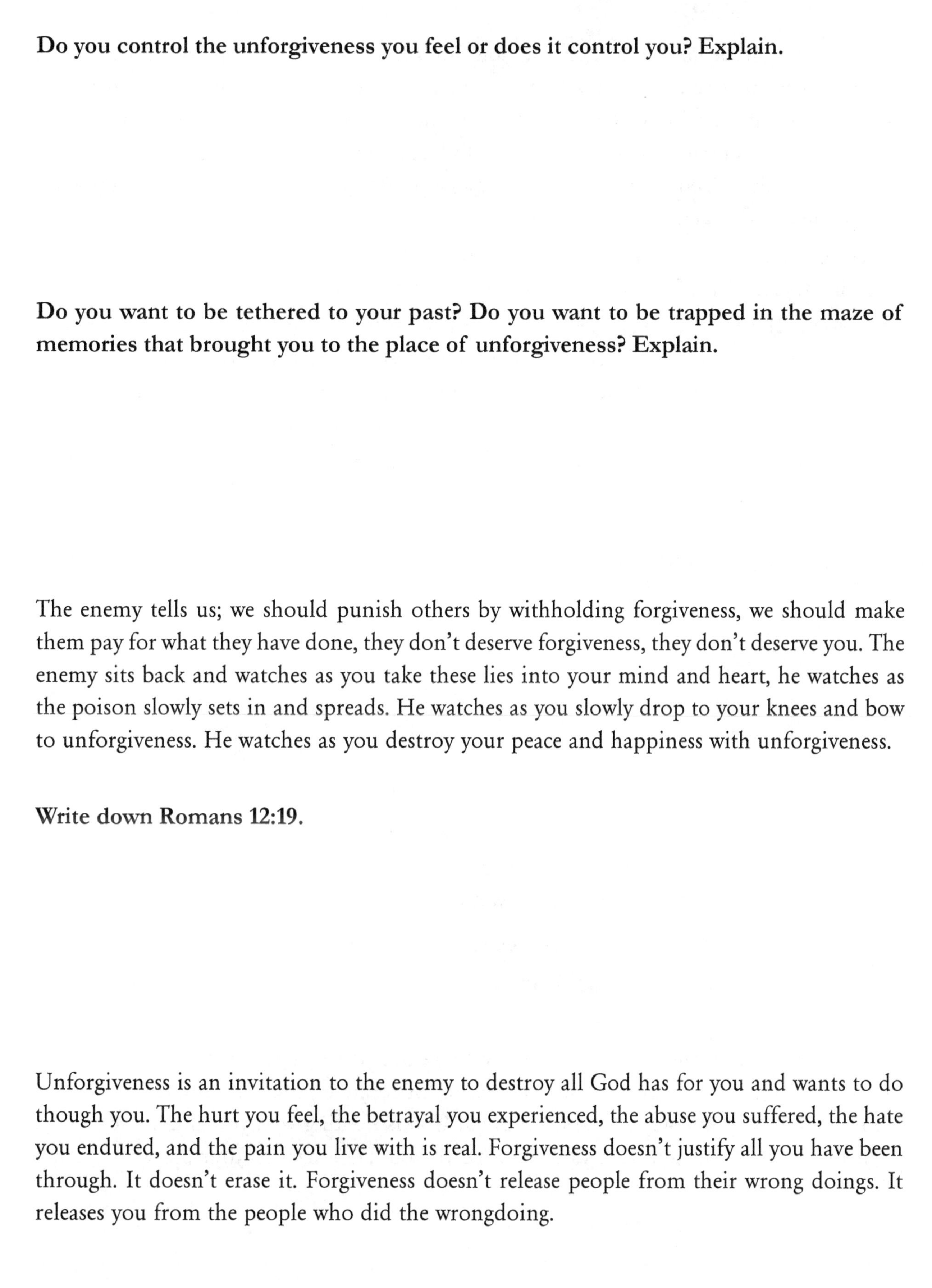

Do you control the unforgiveness you feel or does it control you? Explain.

Do you want to be tethered to your past? Do you want to be trapped in the maze of memories that brought you to the place of unforgiveness? Explain.

The enemy tells us; we should punish others by withholding forgiveness, we should make them pay for what they have done, they don't deserve forgiveness, they don't deserve you. The enemy sits back and watches as you take these lies into your mind and heart, he watches as the poison slowly sets in and spreads. He watches as you slowly drop to your knees and bow to unforgiveness. He watches as you destroy your peace and happiness with unforgiveness.

Write down Romans 12:19.

Unforgiveness is an invitation to the enemy to destroy all God has for you and wants to do though you. The hurt you feel, the betrayal you experienced, the abuse you suffered, the hate you endured, and the pain you live with is real. Forgiveness doesn't justify all you have been through. It doesn't erase it. Forgiveness doesn't release people from their wrong doings. It releases you from the people who did the wrongdoing.

You can't release people from their sin, you don't have that kind of power. To withhold forgiveness because you think it will absolve them of the sin they committed is to believe another lie planted by the enemy. You can only forgive them for what they have done to you. Your forgiveness doesn't take the place of God's forgiveness: after you forgive them, they are still accountable to God. The person (or people) who hurt you must ask God for forgiveness to be completely forgiven.

Write this down: "I don't have the power to absolve sin done by those who have hurt me by forgiving them." Write it as many times it takes to believe it.

The people who hurt you may never confess their sin to God and as a result will never be forgiven for their sin. The same goes for those who choose not to forgive those who have hurt them. You are accountable not for what others have done but for your choice, your decision to forgive or hold on to unforgiveness. Why is forgiveness so important? Because unforgiveness is a wall between you and God's forgiveness of your sin. You cannot be forgiven if you do not forgive.

Write down Matthew 6:14-15

"If you forgive those who sin against you,
your heavenly Father will forgive you.
But if you refuse to forgive others,
your Father will not forgive your sins."
Matthew 6:14-15 NLT

You can start your forgiveness journey today. You can make a choice for freedom, peace, joy and God's forgiveness with the singular decision of forgiving those who have hurt you. It won't be easy, it's not always instantaneous but God is fighting with you and for you. He is right there beside you and he is so very proud of you. He longs for your prayers to sound like this:

"and forgive us our sins, as we have forgiven those who sin against us."
Matthew 6:12 NLT

Below write a prayer of honesty to God, tell him who has hurt you and why you have chosen either forgiveness or unforgiveness.

SILENCED BY UNFORGIVENESS

Study - Reflect - Pray

WEEK FOUR | DAY TWO

Write an honest prayer telling God why you are hanging on to unforgiveness.

Look up and write down scriptures that will encourage, help, convict and motivate you to forgive.

A.

B.

C.

SILENCING UNFORGIVENESS

WEEK FOUR | DAY THREE

Unforgiveness is easy, all you have to do is ride the wave of your feelings. You don't have to decide not to forgive you just have to feed unforgiveness. You have to replay the offense over and over, you have to get mad over and over. You have to allow your sinful human nature to take over and take you wherever it wants to go. All you have to do is bow to unforgiveness and it's yours for as long as you want it.

Forgiveness is hard. You have to discipline your mind and heart, you have to acknowledge that you chose unforgiveness; it didn't choose you. You have to fight your sinful nature and not allow it to take you, your life, your joy, and your heart. You have to stand up to unforgiveness, harness it, take it captive and face it with Jesus. This is the hardest part; facing unforgiveness. It hurts to look at it and realize; unforgiveness didn't happen to you. Hurt, betrayal, abuse, neglect, and pain happened to you, but unforgiveness didn't. The first step to forgiveness is acknowledging that unforgiveness is a choice and you have willingly made it.

Write these words below: Unforgiveness didn't happen to me, I chose it.

We are not victims of unforgiveness; we are volunteers.

Are you ready to harness unforgiveness and bring it down to a bow at Jesus' feet? Explain.

You need to decide to look unforgiveness in the eye and face it, determined to put all the energy you were investing into unforgiveness and put it toward forgiveness.

Most people are looking for the quick fix to forgiveness; I have found that it is a long journey, it is forgiving the person/people that hurt you over and over again. Even though in reality the hurt you suffered is over, your heart and head won't want to let it go, we involuntarily replay the scene in our minds and each time we have to say, "I forgive you."

There will be times when tears will stream down your face when you say those words and other times, you will say them through gritted teeth, but say them every time and you will begin to feel unforgiveness releasing its grip around your heart. The absolute best place to be is when you want to heal from the hurt, trauma, abuse, rejection or betrayal more than you want to hang on to unforgiveness.

Do you want to heal more than you want to hang on to unforgiveness? Explain.

Do you want wholeness and peace? Do you want to win or do you want unforgiveness to win? You will win by forgiving. Harboring unforgiveness is a way of holding on to the past. You can be free, you can live your life with peace and forgiveness, and you can leave your past where it belongs: in your past.

Let's take the first step to forgiveness. Write these words below.

"I forgive you ____________." Write this for each person you need to forgive.

Write down Matthew 18:21-22

You may have to put this exercise into practice many, many times, you may have to forgive the same person seventy times seven but the benefits of forgiveness outweigh the consequences of unforgiveness.

<u>The enemy will use the trauma of your life to keep you from forgiving so he can keep you from being forgiven.</u>

"If you forgive those who sin against you,
your heavenly Father will forgive you.
But if you refuse to forgive others,
your Father will not forgive your sins."
Matthew 6:14-15 NLT

I used to hate this scripture. It left no room for my special circumstance, my hurt, my pain; it left no room for unforgiveness. I wanted a way to hang on to unforgiveness and still be forgiven. I wanted God to take away the pain of unforgiveness while allowing me to still hold on to it. This scripture makes it crystal clear how forgiveness works. He makes it clear so we don't misunderstand the importance of forgiveness. His desire is to forgive you. That is why he sent Jesus to die for us, but just as important, he wants us to forgive each other. God takes forgiveness seriously; he knows it will set you free, he knows it has set you free. God sent his Son to die for our sins so we could have forgiveness at the drop of a prayer, spoken from a heart of repentance.

Write down Philippians 4:6-7.

When I am feeling overwhelmed, angry, hurt, sad or feeling the lure of unforgiveness beckoning me, every single time and without fail, I recite this scripture, I replace the thoughts I'm having with this prayer and I put into practice these simple steps.

1. Don't worry about anything.
2. Pray about everything.
3. Tell God what you need.
4. Thank him for all he's done.

These four steps unlock the peace you are so badly craving. I know from experience that if you genuinely follow the scriptures, *then* you will experience God's peace. His peace cannot be taken away from you, it can't be refuted, and it can't be argued. He gives it to you as a gift. You get to own peace, enjoy it and bask in it. But God is a God of above and beyond, he takes it a step further and he says: "*His peace will guard your hearts and minds as you live in Christ Jesus.*" His peace will stand guard at the entrance of your heart and mind; his peace will not allow unforgiveness, anger or hurt in. His peace will keep your heart at peace.

Do you want peace? Explain.

SILENCING UNFORGIVENESS

Study - Reflect - Pray

WEEK FOUR | DAY FOUR

"Don't worry about anything; instead, pray about everything.
Tell God what you need, and thank him for all he has done.
Then you will experience God's peace,
which exceeds anything we can understand.
His peace will guard your hearts and minds as you live in Christ Jesus."
Philippians 4:6-7 NLT

Today you are going to put into practice this scripture step by step.

Don't worry about anything; INSTEAD

"Pray about everything" – Write down your "everything" below.

"Tell God what you need" – Write down what you need.

"Thank him for all he has done" – Write your prayer of thanksgiving.

SILENCED BY UNFORGIVENESS

No Longer

WEEK FOUR | DAY FIVE

"I will praise the LORD at all times. I will constantly speak his praises."
Psalm 34:1 NLT

Forgiveness is freedom.

Freedom to be forgiven, freedom from bowing to unforgiveness, freedom from pain, hurt, and your past. Freedom from the person who hurt you, freedom to share the message of Jesus' forgiveness with others and freedom to change the world for Jesus.

What freedom would you like to experience when you forgive those who have hurt you? Explain.

The enemy knows the power of forgiveness and he knows the way to distract you from leading others to the forgiveness of Jesus is to keep you from forgiving. He thinks he can outsmart us, he thinks that if he can tempt us, we can't resist it. The scripture below outed him. It gave us his battle plan and it disempowered him and empowered us.

"...when I forgive whatever needs to be forgiven,
I do so with Christ's authority for your benefit,
so that Satan will not outsmart us.
For we are familiar with his evil schemes."
2 Corinthians 2:10-11 NLT

The enemy wants to use unforgiveness to silence you, he thinks he can outsmart you with his evil scheme and temptation to harbor unforgiveness. He thinks he can win and he can, *if* you let him. *You* have to determine to win, *you* have to determine to forgive.

Do you want the enemy to lose? Do you want to win this battle? Explain.

You are not defined by what happened to you, but by your willingness to forgive. Forgiving others will transform your life and as a result you can transform your world and then together, we can transform the world for Jesus.

Do you believe that our world needs to see forgiveness modeled? Explain.

In your opinion what would change in our world if all Christian women modeled forgiveness? Explain.

I want to remind you that we were created on purpose and with a purpose. We were created to change the world around us for Jesus. We were not created to be changed by the world, or our circumstances, pain, hurt, betrayal, or experiences. We were not created to sit in pain and wallow in unforgiveness, and we were not created to bow and be immobilized by the pain of our past and our unwillingness to forgive.

Have you allowed the world to change you or are you changing the world? Explain.

God has a plan to reach the world through us, but he needs us whole, healed, redeemed, restored, forgiven, and forgiving so he can change the world through us. This unforgiving world needs to see Jesus through our forgiveness, and it needs to know that there is hope of forgiveness through Jesus no matter what they have done. They need to know that the women of God's army will not judge or condemn them for their past but instead lead them to the one who wants to forgive them.

Our responsibility as Christ followers is to model forgiveness. Jesus died for our sins, he died to be able to forgive us at the same rate as our asking for it. He planned on forgiving us by dying on the cross long before we were born, and long before we asked for forgiveness. We have never been asked to die or pay for the forgiveness of other's offense but we are asked to forgive for free and with no payment on our part or theirs.

This is what we share with a world that is used to paying a price for everything. When we forgive, we can confidently talk about Jesus forgiveness of our sins and we can offer them the same hope and freedom. We can share this scripture with confidence.

Write down 1 John 1:9.

Living a life free from unforgiveness is beautiful. It allows you to see the hurt of the world through the lenses of forgiveness, to see another's pain instead of your own. It frees you up from feeling sorry for yourself when you see their pain. Instead of comparing your pain, you compare your healing to their pain. That comparison will inspire you to introduce them to Jesus; the one who can rescue them from their pain, and the one who can lead them to forgiveness and freedom.

We are not victims of unforgiveness: we are volunteer to forgive.

We, the Christian women of the world, volunteer to forgive those who have hurt us, abandoned us, neglected us, betrayed us, abused us, belittled us, used us, forgotten us, ignored us, humiliated us, and those who did not defend us.

List the offenses you choose to forgive.

We forgive so we can be forgiven, and we forgive because we have been forgiven. We forgive so we can have freedom, and so we can share the power of forgiveness with a world that has bowed to unforgiveness. We forgive because we know the short-term pain of forgiveness is better than a lifetime of pain caused by unforgiveness. We choose to walk in the freedom paid for on the cross by our Savior.

The statement above is a powerful declaration that can become your motto when the need to forgive arises. In the space below, personalize this declaration.

We are the army of God–the army that marches with the banner of forgiveness. With confidence, we pray for forgiveness for our sins against you because we have forgiven those who have sinned against us.

"and forgive us our sins, as we have forgiven those who sin against us."
Matthew 6:12 NLT

When you choose to no longer be silenced by unforgiveness but instead choose to stand in the face of it, you are not alone. God is standing right beside you. He stands next to you and says, "Now this is a girl I can change the world through."

_______________________ is a girl God can change the world through!

SILENCED BY SHAME

WEEK FIVE | DAY ONE

We, the Christian women of this world, are a silenced army. Silenced by shame. We humans have a sin problem. We are stubborn, prideful, selfish, fearful, doubtful, lazy, addicted, jealous, and deceitful. I can go on and on so let's just call it like it is: –sinful.

Write down Romans 3:23.

This verse puts us all in the same category of sinner. We all have done things that we are ashamed of, we have all let God and people down. We all have those cringeworthy and shameful memories of what we have done and are desperate to forget. We all have sinned and fallen short of God's glorious standard.

A silenced army: every single one of us volunteers, every single one of us sinners.

The silenced army is an army plagued with the aftermath of sin, silenced by shame, guilt, worthlessness, and brokenness. This is an army stripped of its weapons and replaced with weights and chains.

Have you or do you feel the weight of shame? Explain.

Your struggle with shame is not an accident: This is a strategic move by our enemy. A plan tried and true throughout the ages. He happily targets us, tempting us to embrace guilt and shame. He knows shame will destroy all that God has planned to do through us, he knows it will silence us.

Write down John 10:10.

In Genesis chapter 3 we read about Satan's deliberate targeting of Eve because she was the missing piece in his plan. She was the piece he needed to bring sin into our world. He needed her to bring shame on an entire gender so we would become a silenced army: an army reminded of sin and shamed because of it. The ashamed army is an ineffective army, an immobile army, a scattered army: it is a silenced army.

Eve wasn't his only target of our gender. You are a target. You and your purpose to change the world for Jesus. You and your story of surrender to Jesus–your admission of sin and acceptance of his forgiveness. You and your voice.

You and your willingness to act when your purpose and the need for it collide.

You are a target.

Did you know that Satan will use shame to silence you? Explain.

Satan doesn't just need you to bring sin into the world; he needs you to be silenced by the sin in your world, the same sin forgiven and forgotten by our Savior. Jesus saw your sin and went to the cross as a volunteer. He stood up and said, "I will pay the price. I will take on her shame, guilt, brokenness, and sin. I will bear the burden, so she doesn't have to." Jesus knew the burden would be too much for you to carry. He knew the weight of sin and shame would make you bow to them.

Write down 1 Peter 2:24.

Jesus was not a victim of the cross, he was a volunteer so that you wouldn't have to be a victim of sin and shame, but a volunteer to change the world.

"No one can take my life from me. I sacrifice it voluntarily.
For I have the authority to lay it down when I want to and also to take it up again.
For this is what my Father has commanded."
John 10:18 NLT

We know Jesus died for our sin and abolished the shame attached to it but for some of us, the solution to our shame is just too easy of a solution. What Jesus did for us isn't "good enough:" it doesn't feel significant enough, so we choose to carry the shame of sins, both forgiven and forgotten; we decide to feel the shame of sins Jesus died to erase. We choose to be silenced and weighted down by the sin Jesus volunteered to die for.

Do you pray asking for forgiveness for the same sin/shame over and over again? Explain.

We carry shame in our hearts, allowing it to break us over and over, and we wrap the chains of guilt and shame around us like a blanket, refusing to let go. All the while Satan watches and thanks us for silencing ourselves. Shame in all its forms holds us back. It silences us and bottles up the purpose inside of us, locking it away.

Do you allow shame to dictate how you fell about yourself? Explain.

Shame isn't limited to what we have done or what has been done to us, shame is a tool the enemy uses in as many scenarios as he can. He wants you to feel shame for being a woman, for being a leader, a preacher or teacher, for being strong, for following Christ wholeheartedly in the midst of a world that rejects him, for being single, a single mom, or a divorcee. He wants you to feel the false shame of thinking you are being a bad mom, wife, daughter, sister, aunt or friend. He will use anything in your life to tempt you to attach shame to it.

What are you ashamed of? Explain.

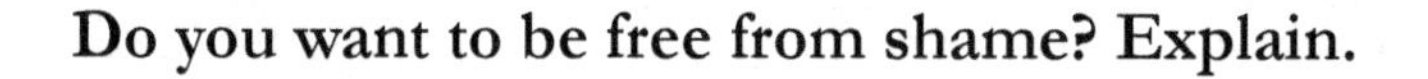

Do you want to be free from shame? Explain.

God did not create you to feel ashamed. He didn't plan your life, purpose, and calling to be infused with shame. He never asked you to carry shame in fact he told you not too. He went to great lengths on the way to the cross and on the cross to free you from shame.

Write a prayer below confessing your shame to God, give it to him so he can receive it and then forget it.

SILENCED BY SHAME

Study - Reflect - Pray

WEEK FIVE | DAY TWO

"I will forgive their wickedness and will remember their sins no more."
Hebrews 8:12 NIV

1. **Write truths about shame below. (example: Shame is a lie from the enemy. Shame is not from God. Shame is a tactic of the enemy to keep me silent.)**

2. **Look up and write down a scripture that will encourage you to release your shame.**

3. **Look up and write down a scripture that will bring freedom, healing, peace and joy to your mind, heart and life.**

SILENCING SHAME

WEEK FIVE | DAY THREE

Silencing shame will give voice to your calling and purpose. Satan doesn't want you to know this: he doesn't want you to find freedom from shame. He knows he can be defeated, Satan knows Jesus died on the cross to free us from shame. He was there, and he saw what Jesus did. Satan knows freedom is found in Jesus, and he knows that you are so close to finding out that you don't have to live this way, so he whispers reminders of your past and present to you. If you choose to listen you have been effectively silenced.
Jesus will never bring shame or guilt into your life. He gives freedom, forgiveness, hope, healing, and restoration freely to all who ask and receive it.

Write the statement above in the space below. Personalize it to you.

Sometimes we get stuck after we receive forgiveness. We know we are forgiven but we refuse to accept it, instead we choose to torture ourselves with shame. The enemy comes to you day and night judging you for your sin, bringing out of the shadows all of your mistakes, fears, doubts, insecurities, brokenness, guilt, and sin. He parades them in front of your worst accuser–YOU. You play back the scenes that have rendered you guilty, and you sentence yourself to a life of shame and silence.

Read John 8:1-11

In this passage we see three different stories playing out in front of us. The first story line is that of the woman. During that time in history if a woman was caught in adultery the only consequence was death. She must have been terrified as they put her in front of the crowd and asked the man who was teaching if she should be stoned. Can you imagine standing there dreading the words to come and the death sentence to follow? She listened as the men who brought her to Jesus grew more agitated, as they demanded an answer, as they demanded that he speak the words that would condemn her to death–the words everyone except her were waiting to hear.

The second story line is of the accusers. In this case we can replace the accusers with the enemy. He watches and waits for his moment to accuse you of a crime both committed and not! Innocent or guilty, doesn't matter to him. His motive is to humiliate you, punish you, accuse you and silence you.

The third story line is of Jesus' love, mercy, grace and forgiveness. What a powerful picture of grace when Jesus stood up for the woman. He stood up with the guilty woman, and he stood up for the guilty woman. He stood up to her accusers and said, "All right, but let the one who has never sinned throw the first stone!"

After all of her accusers had walked away, Jesus stood again. He looked at this guilty and shamed woman and asked, "Where are your accusers? Didn't even one of them condemn you?"

With a shaky voice she answers him with a simple, "No, Lord." This guilty woman never expresses remorse, never apologized or tried to explain her side of the story, and she never even begged for mercy or promised never to sin again. Jesus in all of his grace, love, and mercy tells her, "Neither do I. Go and sin no more."

Jesus said to the guilty and shamed woman, I do not condemn you, you are set free. Jesus knows your heart; he knows who you are on the inside. I believe he saw this woman's heart and saw she was repentant, so he forgave her and released her from sin and shame. He knows your heart, he knows you are repentant and he has released you from sin and shame.

If your shame stems not from sin but from sins against you or an accusing voice in your head meant only to silence you, your battle is the same as those who are being rightly accused. Shame knows no boundaries, sees no color, and is indifferent to age or gender. It has one goal and one goal only: to silence you.

Write these words below, "Jesus does not condemn me."

Write these words below, "I am set free."

Write these words below, "Shame has lost its power."

"If we confess our sins to him,
he is faithful and just to forgive us our sins
and to cleanse us from all wickedness."
1 John 1:9 NLT

She saw firsthand his faithfulness to forgive, but she was still guilty. His forgiveness didn't erase time and her memory, so how could she not be condemned for her sin?

Write down Hebrews 8:12

He forgave her and remembered her sin no more. He stood with a woman free of sin, guilt, and shame. She was made new and whole in the eyes of Jesus. He has done the same for you.

Write down Psalm 32:5

Jesus stood upright on the cross for all to see, and he did it for you. On that cross, he stood up with you, he stood up for you, and he stood up to your accusers.

The second you asked Jesus to forgive you he accepted your plea and forgave you. From that moment on, he sees a forgiven, clean, whole, and healed woman, with not an accuser in sight. His sacrifice gave us the freedom to no longer live as victims of sin, but volunteers to be free of guilt and shame.

Jesus silenced sin and shame: he has silenced your accusers. Now it is your turn. It is time for you to release shame and embrace freedom. It is time to accept that God has forgiven and forgotten your sin and shame. You are now a new, clean, whole, forgiven and cleansed daughter.

Write a prayer releasing your shame and guilt to God.

SILENCING SHAME

Study - Reflect - Pray

WEEK FIVE | DAY FOUR

"For it is with your heart that you believe and are justified,
and it is with your mouth that you profess your faith and are saved.
As Scripture says, 'Anyone who believes in him will never be put to shame.'"
Romans 10:10-11 NIV

Look up and write down scriptures of freedom.

1.

2.

Write three action steps you will take to silence shame when it tries to sneak back into your life.

1.

2.

3.

Write a prayer to God. Tell him what is on your heart; your fears, concerns, worries, hurt, shame, excitement, thanksgiving, motivation, etc.

SILENCED BY SHAME

No Longer

WEEK FIVE | DAY FIVE

"And now, dear brothers and sisters, one final thing.
Fix your thoughts on what is true, and honorable, and right, and pure,
and lovely, and admirable. Think about things that are excellent and worthy of praise."
Philippians 4:8 NLT

We, the Christian women of the world, have been gifted freedom. We are no longer silenced by sin and shame; instead, we are the front line of hope, we are the face of healing, and we are the voice of Jesus on earth. We have the privilege of claiming freedom from shame and we have the responsibility to share this freedom with those who are silenced by shame.

Write down John 8:36

Write these worlds below: "I am free."

We the Christian women of the world are free, now it is time to join the battle to change the world for Jesus. Free to share the message of Jesus, this message is powerful enough to replace lies with truth in their hearts and minds, bring hope to the hopeless, healing to the sick and broken, joy to the depressed, peace to the anxious, direction to the lost, significance to the unseen, a hearing ear to the unheard, freedom to the enslaved, and Heaven to the Hell-bound.

God has released you from shame so you can change the world for him. What specifically are you free to do? (you can use the list above for inspiration or a guide.)

We are the forgiven and free, the healed and restored, the unashamed and unafraid, bringing the message of Jesus to the lost and bound, broken and sick, the ashamed and afraid, and the accused and condemned.

Write down Isaiah 61:7

The NLT version of this verse says, "Instead of shame and dishonor, you will enjoy a double share of honor. You will possess a double portion of prosperity in your land, and everlasting joy will be yours." This accurately describes what happens when you silence shame and use the voice God has given you.

What has God done for you that shame has kept silent within you? Explain.

If shame doesn't silence you what does? Explain.

We can't be afraid or ashamed to bring these rare and precious gifts to a world that so badly needs them. With a shame-free life, we are required to share all that God can and will do for our world, and we have to use the shame-free voice we have been given with courage and boldness.

Look up and write down a scripture that will give you courage and boldness to use your voice when silence would be easier.

You don't have to be courageous and bold every minute of your life, you just need to silence shame and embrace courage and boldness when the opportunity to use your voice and the need for it collide.

Can you commit to doing your absolute best to silence shame in your heart and head when you know it is time to use your voice to share your God story? Explain.

It is easier to commit to the question above when you wholeheartedly accept that Jesus stood upright on the cross for all to see, and he did it for you. On that cross, he stood up with you, he stood up for you, and he stood up to your accusers. This message, purpose, and calling that is rooted in your heart has to be shared with the world.

"No one lights a lamp and then puts it under a basket.
Instead, a lamp is placed on a stand,
where it gives light to everyone in the house.
In the same way,
let your good deeds shine out for all to see,
so that everyone will praise your heavenly Father."
Matthew 5:15-16 NLT

You are a light. You shine bright in the darkness drawing those who are lost to the light they see in you.

Shame cannot be the reason you put your light under a basket, hiding it from a world that so badly needs the same light in their lives, not when Jesus took our and their shame and bore it for us. We are forgiven, guilt-free, shame-free, set free, redeemed, and delivered. We are not victims of shame, instead we are volunteers to silence it–free to use our voice to share freedom with a world chained to shame.

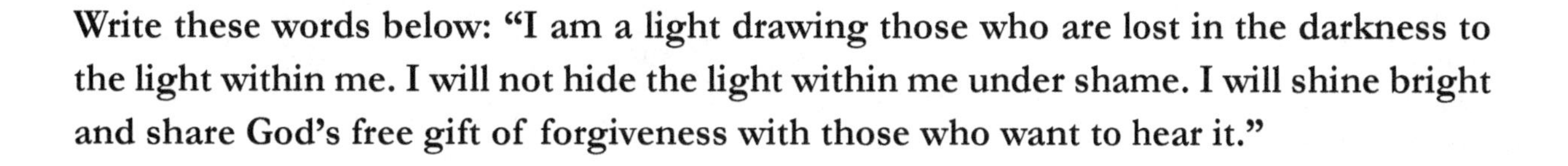

Write these words below: "I am a light drawing those who are lost in the darkness to the light within me. I will not hide the light within me under shame. I will shine bright and share God's free gift of forgiveness with those who want to hear it."

We all have fears real or imagined of what will happen if we silence shame and transparently talk about what God has freed us from and forgiven us for. We know God has forgiven and forgotten our sin but we also know that humans have a longer memory, less grace, and more opinions on our past and present. This knowledge of how people operate can bring or add to the shame we already struggle to silence.

What do you fear will happen if you use your voice to talk about things that you were shamed by? Explain.

What could happen if you share the freedom you have after you silenced shame with someone who is silenced by shame? Explain.

Write down Joshua 1:9.

When you choose to no longer be silenced by sin, shame, and guilt, and instead choose to stand in the face of it, you are not alone. God is standing right beside you. He stands there next to you and says, "Now this is a girl I can change the world through."

______________________ is a girl God can change the world through!

SILENCED BY OFFENSE

WEEK SIX | DAY ONE

We, the Christian women of this world, are a silenced army. Silenced by offense.

Offended by the church.
Offended by the pastor.
Offended by people.
Offended by God.

Are you offended by any of the above? Explain.

I recently heard a speaker say that women today are balancing on a three-legged stool. The first leg represents their family, the second leg represents their faith, and the third leg represents their career/vocation. If she doesn't balance correctly, she will come crashing down.

Do you feel your life is a balancing act? Explain.

She: the wife, mom, sister, daughter, aunt, grandma, caregiver.

She: the overworked, underappreciated, stressed-out, stretched thin, overcommitted, and overlooked woman.

Do any of the above describe you? Explain.

I see this balancing act more and more by single moms, married moms, single ladies, married ladies, divorced moms, divorced ladies, widowed moms, and widowed ladies. The list of circumstances, titles and responsibilities a lady now has left the church struggling to keep up and asking the question, "How do I speak to every single one of these scenarios in one hour, once a week?"

Do you feel your unique situation is addressed in a church service setting? Explain.

The answer to the question, "How can pastors speak to every single different struggle, circumstance, title and responsibility in one hour one day a week" is ... they can't!

The latest research shows that this challenge is affecting women's attendance to church. Women are choosing not to attend at all, because they no longer fit into the traditional role talked about in church. When the church (the people in the church) offend us there is a very thin line that is often crossed. This line divides being offended by people from being offended by God. We often give up on God because people, the church, or religion offends us.

Are you ever tempted to give up on God when people or the church offends you? Explain.

Women are feeling slighted, overlooked, marginalized, forgotten, and underrepresented in the church world, and they choose to be offended. Tired of only being offered volunteer positions in the nursery or kids' ministry, women protest by not volunteering at all. Tired of not seeing their gender represented on the stage, women protest with their generosity. Tired of not hearing a message tailor-fit for women, they protest with their attendance. Tired of feeling left out by the other women in the church or disconnected from the "people in the know" many women protest by not attending Bible studies, small groups or events specifically designed to help connect women.

Have you ever or are you currently holding back your gifts, talents or tithe/offering because you feel offended? Explain.

"An offended friend is harder to win back than a fortified city.
Arguments separate friends like a gate locked with bars."
Proverbs 18:19 NLT

Women silenced by offense are comparing the church to the world and finding the church falls short. This is a lie, a false truth and the enemy's plan is in full effect. The enemy loves when we are offended because he knows the scripture above (Proverbs 18:19) is true. He knows that silencing offense is a long, hard road, so he encourages us and tempts us to hang on tightly to offense.

Offended Christian women are asking these two questions in our church's today; *Where do I fit in? Where are the people like me?*

Do you ever find yourself asking either or both of these questions? Explain.

Silently, thousands of ladies leave empty seats in churches around the world.

Silenced by offense.

Silenced by offense they will find everything wrong with the church, while those who silence offense will find everything right with the church.

When people purposely go out of their way to offend you it is their choice, but *holding on* to offense and choosing to harbor it is your choice. We are not victims of offense, we are volunteers.

Do you voluntarily hang on to offense? Explain.

When we voluntarily hang on to offense, we silence ourselves. Offense isn't happy with taking our peace: it has to grow into anger, then into bitterness, and then into unforgiveness. Each of these things is planned by the enemy to make sure you stay silent and to keep you from changing the world for Jesus. When you are busy being offended you are distracted from what God wants to do in you and through you.

Read Ephesians 4:22-27.

Write down verses 26 and 27.

As far as I can tell you have to get rid of anger and offense before bedtime. If you are anything like me you need a few hours to be angry so take some time during the day to be angry but confess it and release it as quickly as you can and as the scriptures command, before bedtime. If you don't verse 27 clearly states, "For anger gives a foothold to the devil." No one wants to give a foothold to the enemy but that is exactly what we are doing. In fact, we invite him to have a foothold when we harbor offense and allow it to grow into anger.

We are complicated human beings in fact Psalm 139:14 says we are "wonderfully complex." I don't think David (the author) was only referring to the functions and intricacies of our bodies but also to our minds and feelings. Humans are bound to offend and we are bound to be offended, but we have the choice and power to silence offense, we have the authority to stop the enemy from having a foot hold and we have the mandate to use our unoffended voice to change the world for Jesus.

There is one cure to the plague of offense, and it is found in Colossians 3:2. Write it below.

You are not a victim of offense. You are a volunteer to silence it!

SILENCED BY OFFENSE

Study - Reflect - Pray

WEEK SIX | DAY TWO

1. **What does the Bible instruct you to do when someone offends you? Explain.**

2. **Is being offended a choice? ________________.**

3. If you made allowances for others to have faults what would change in your mind, heart and attitude toward them. Explain.

"Make allowance for each other's faults, and forgive anyone who offends you. Remember, the Lord forgave you, so you must forgive others."

Colossians 3:13 NLT

4. Write a prayer confessing to God all the times you have chosen to be offended or forgiveness. Ask him to forgive you and to remind you to give allowances for each other's faults.

SILENCING OFFENSE

WEEK SIX | DAY THREE

She: the wife, mom, sister, daughter, aunt, grandma, and caregiver.

She: the hardworking, works out when stressed out, multitasker extraordinaire, committed, bold, determined, and courageous woman.

Day one of this week you were silenced by offense, but not anymore: you are a volunteer to silence offense! You are a women who is determined to see the church as God intended it to be seen.

The world tells us that women have shattered the glass ceiling, but all she sees is the damage that the falling glass leaves behind. She sees the collateral damage of pitting women against men, women against women, and men against men—all in the name of progress. There is the perception that church women are dealing with a dropped ceiling; however, she doesn't see a ceiling, she sees clear blue skies made by her creator. She sees endless possibilities to serve her community and to change the world around her for Jesus.

Silencing offense will open your eyes to the power of the church and to those who are lost in the church.

If you silenced offense in your heart right now, what good would you see in the church? Explain.

You compare the church to the world and find the church to be a safe place, a refuge, and a comfort. You see the world for what it is: cold and unforgiving, judgmental, superficial and distracting.

You walk into a church where women are sitting alone in their loneliness, hurt, and brokenness, waiting to be comforted by the words of the songs to come and inspired by the message preached. You never have to ask where you fit in, because everyone fits in, and everyone is there for the same reason—to have an encounter with God, to learn and grow, to be encouraged, motivated, and challenged, and healed and heard by God. Everywhere you look there are people just like you.

Silently, thousands of ladies just like you fill empty seats in churches around the world.

How can you make a difference for a lady who may feel alone in a church setting? Explain.

When we silence offense, we can volunteer to help others do the same. The solution is as simple as identifying what offended you and working to eliminate that problem for others.

What offends you? Explain.

What can you do to eliminate this problem in your sphere of influence for others? Explain.

The church will never get everything right. It will always be messy, offend, and often make mistakes, because the church is not a building, the church is the people. We are the people that make up the church, and we don't always get everything right. We are messy and are bound to offend someone. We are human and we make mistakes.

Write this down: "I am the church."

One of the biggest complaints and reasons women are offended that I keep hearing is that the messages in church settings speak to traditional gender roles that used to be held by the gender that traditionally held the positions, title or responsibilities.

Now we have women who are CEOs and men who are stay-at-home dads. We have women who are the breadwinners and heads of household for their families and men who are raising their kids alone. We have young people who are choosing not to get married and married couples who are choosing not to have kids. The traditional family is not so traditional anymore. So how do we stay unoffended when the message on Sunday morning is tailor-fit for the dwindling traditional family?

The church can't be expected to answer all our questions, speak to our unique situation, or share infinite wisdom; the church is comprised of people, limited in answers, limited to their experiences, and limited to one hour on Sunday. However, God is available 24/7. He is all knowing, possessing all the answers, willing and waiting to share them with you.

Write down James 1:5.

God will share his wisdom with you generously, but your faith must be in God alone. We can address every trouble and struggle in our lives with the Word of God and in prayer. The answers, encouragement, help, hope, and support are all at our fingertips.

It is easier to be offended, and it is easier to silence the solutions we have available than it is to put effort into finding them. When I was offended and hanging on to my offense for dear life, I didn't want answers; I wanted to be mad. I didn't want to seek Jesus; I wanted him brought to me. I wanted it to happen my way. I was wrong.

What ways can you contextualize the message, preaching, or teaching to fit your unique situation? Explain.

One great tool I've picked up is; taking notes. I am a female pastor, the founder of a ministry, an author and speaker, most seminars for these titles and accomplishments are for male pastors, leaders, and speakers so naturally every gender reference is male. In my notes I write *she* or *her* instead of *he* or *him*, I contextualize it to me. I could sit there offended, but instead I take the great message, tools, helps, and direction and receive them because it doesn't matter who is being referenced, if it applies to you then it is good for you.

Silencing offense allows you to hear what God is saying to you. The enemy's purpose is to kill, steal, and destroy and he will use offense to steal from you, to steal what God has to say to you.

Today is a good day to silence offense!

SILENCING OFFENSE

Study - Reflect - Pray

WEEK SIX | DAY FOUR

"Ask and it will be given to you; seek and you will find; knock and the door will be opened to you."
Matthew 7:7 NIV

1. **Write down Proverbs 4:23.**

2. **Why do you need to guard your heart from offense?**

    1.

    2.

    3.

3. **Write a prayer asking God to help you silence offense and to see the needs of the people around you. Ask him to reveal to you when you can be a part of the solution and ask him for the courage to do it.**

SILENCED BY OFFENSE

No Longer

WEEK SIX | DAY FIVE

"Think about the things of heaven, not the things of earth."
Colossians 3:2 NLT

We, the Christian women of the world, are silencing offense so we can change the world for Jesus.

We understand that what we let into our hearts we will give to the world. If we let offense in, we will give offense to the world. If we let encouragement in, we will give encouragement to the world. If we allow God to change us, we will bring that same change into our world.

We can choose offense, or we can choose to silence it. We can choose to become the obstacle that keeps the beautiful message of Jesus from being shared with the world, or we can be the army who removes the obstacle of offense and bravely, boldly, and confidently stands up for Jesus and steps into our purpose and calling.

Each one of us equipped and purposed to change the world for Jesus, and each one of us is a crucial part of the church.

"In his grace, God has given us different gifts for doing certain things well.
So if God has given you the ability to prophesy, speak out with as much faith as God has given you. If your gift is serving others, serve them well. If you are a teacher, teach well. If your gift is to encourage others, be encouraging. If it is giving, give generously.
If God has given you leadership ability, take the responsibility seriously.

And if you have a gift for showing kindness to others, do it gladly.
Don't just pretend to love others. Really love them. Hate what is wrong. Hold tightly to what is good. Love each other with genuine affection, and take delight in honoring each other. Never be lazy, but work hard and serve the Lord enthusiastically.
Rejoice in our confident hope. Be patient in trouble, and keep on praying.
When God's people are in need, be ready to help them."
Romans 12:6-13 NLT

What gifts and abilities are listed in the scripture above? List them.

1.

2.

3.

4.

5.

6.

7.

8.

When you silence offense, you can do what the scripture above says you can: "*Love each other with genuine affection, and take delight in honoring each other."*

The enemy would love nothing more than to see the church destroy itself from the inside out. He would love for women to be offended and silenced. He would love for you to think that your purpose can only be lived out within the walls of the church building. He would love for you to believe that the only way to fulfill your purpose is through the volunteer positions that are offered. He would love to see you limited by rules and tradition.

The eight gifts and abilities are all meant to be used inside and outside of the church.

Below list the gifts and abilities you have.

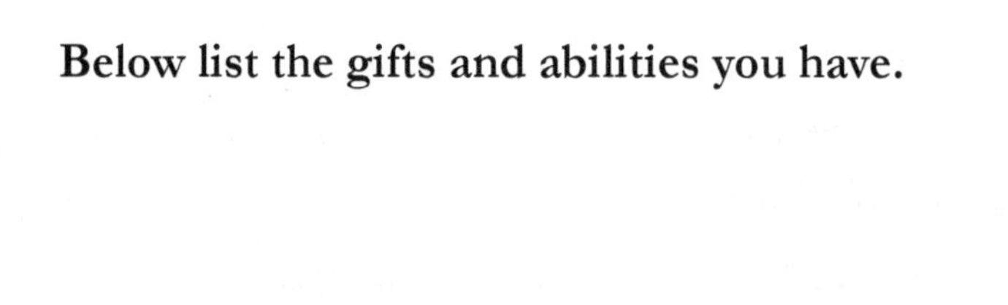

How can you use them inside and outside of the church? Explain.

There are no limits with God. There are no walls, no traditions. There is only obedience and submission, calling and purpose, and the mandate to not just serve in the church, but to also leave the walls of the church and GO into all the world and preach, share, and spread the good news of Jesus.

"And then he told them,
'Go into all the world and preach the Good News to everyone.'"
Mark 16:15 NLT

We, the women of the church, are created on purpose and for a purpose. We were created to change the world for Jesus by being the church and created to step into our purpose and take the message of Jesus into a lost and broken world. We were chosen to love the church, to be the church, and to leave the walls of the church, taking our God-given purpose and giving it freely to a world that needs it.

This mandate is not easy, silencing offense is not easy, changing the world for Jesus is not easy but **it is possible**! If we, the Christian women of the world, will go into all the world with this scripture in our hearts and minds and not just know this scripture but put it into practice, we can change the world for Jesus.

"Don't just pretend to love others. Really love them. Hate what is wrong. Hold tightly to what is good. Love each other with genuine affection, and take delight in honoring each other. Never be lazy, but work hard and serve the Lord enthusiastically.

Rejoice in our confident hope. Be patient in trouble, and keep on praying.

When God's people are in need, be ready to help them."

Romans 12:9-13 NLT

Which of the above do you struggle with? Explain.

Write down one scripture per struggle that will encourage you, help you and motivate you to silence that struggle in your life.

Offense is a tactic the enemy loves to use against us, he knows it works, he knows it renders God's army powerless but we have a very powerful tactic of our own.

Write down James 4:7.

Offense is a choice but you don't have to give into the temptation, James 4:7 says if you submit yourself to God and resist the devil, (that's right: we need to become the resistance against the devil.) HE WILL FLEE FROM YOU! He is a coward, he is an opportunist, he prowls around looking for someone's, hope, joy, peace, purpose, unity and calling to devour. He is looking to devour our army. Yet we are wise to his tactics we will resist him and he will flee.

Below write a bold prayer of resistance.

When you choose to no longer be silenced by offense, but instead choose to stand in the face of it, you are not alone. God is standing right beside you. He stands next to you and says, "Now this is a girl I can change the world through."

______________________ is a girl God can change the world through!

SILENCED BY PRIDE

WEEK SEVEN | DAY ONE

We, the Christian women of this world, are a silenced army. Silenced by pride. Pride: the downfall of nations, corporations, relationships, marriages, the church, and God's army.

Write down Proverbs 16:18.

Pride steals and destroys our joy, contentment, self-esteem, confidence, hope, peace, and unity.

Pride keeps us comparing and competing, selfish and self-centered, miserable and lonely. Pride thinly veils our fears, vulnerabilities, shame, inadequacies, and insecurities. Pride is a false security that we are safe behind the image we present to the world.

Do you ever present an image that is different than your reality? Explain.

Desperate to hide our faults from the world, we build a tight wall around ourselves leaving no room for anyone else. With pride we wall family and friends out, we wall accountability out, we wall our fellow Christ-follower out, we wall the truth in, and we wall God out.

We bow to pride, and we choose silence.

Pride requires us to compare ourselves to others, our lives to other people's lives, and our accomplishments to other people's accomplishments. If we are constantly comparing ourselves to each other and rendering ourselves less than, we sneak the poison of pride into the troops. The voice of pride will rise up and instead of being confident in who God created us to be, we tear each other down to a level that makes us feel better about ourselves. And the cycle continues in each of us until the poison has spread through the ranks. An army brought down to a bow by pride. Pride will silence the voice of God in our lives and give voice to the enemy.

Do you compare yourself, your life, success, accomplishments, progress, etc. to others? Explain.

Why?

If you conclude that others are better than you, how does this make your feel? Explain.

If you conclude that others are not better than you, how does this make your feel? Explain.

God and pride cannot occupy the same space.
Where there is pride, there is no God.

If God and pride were in the same space, God would outshine it–pride won't let that happen. Pride says I know better than God, that I am better than God. It consumes your thoughts and directs your actions and your life and it leaves no room for God.

Write down Psalm 10:4.

All too often, we believe the lie being fed to us by the enemy: The lie that says we are not equal in God's eyes, and that we are better than some and worse than others.

God's truth is this: We are all loved equally and are treasured, and we were all created with the purpose to change the world for Jesus using the gifts, talents, purpose and calling he created us with. Each one of us is unique and different on purpose, chosen for different assignment, with none more important than the other.

Write down 1 Peter 4:10.

We complicate this simple message with pride: we look at the people around us and rank each other. We compare our lives with theirs. We compare our looks, weight, and fashion; we compare our friends, boyfriends, husbands and kids; we compare our calling and purpose. As a result, we are left unsatisfied. As 1 Peter 4:10 says we are to use the unique gifts we are given to serve each other well, instead we compare these gifts to each other's we allow pride in to destroy what God is trying to do through us.

This lack of satisfaction and contentment with who God made us leads to pride and anger; these emotions compel us to action–pride. Pride will push us to be better than or to make others less than. Women of the world are silencing each other because of pride.

We are not victim of pride; we are volunteers.

Not one of us is immune to pride. One of the pride traps is social media, the spark that ignites pride in many of us. We scroll through snapshots of people's lives, and we compare the entirety of our lives to their snapshot. Unsatisfied with the comparison, we criticize each other for not "being real," authentic, or transparent. We come to the conclusion that their "real" can't be real, because if it is, our "real" is not good enough.

What is a pride trigger in your life? Explain.

Comparison is the thief of joy and contentment–the key that unlocks the door to pride.

Instead of cheering each other on and supporting and encouraging each other, we fight each other in a silent pride war.

The enemy watches, loving every minute of it. He knows that if we are fighting each other, we won't focus on fighting him, and we won't change the world for Jesus. All he has to do is sit back and wait for the fall and our self-imposed destruction.

"Pride goes before destruction, a haughty spirit before a fall."
Proverbs 16:18 NIV

Pride brings destruction to our relationship with God, each other, and the purpose we are supposed to fulfill. It leaves us lost in a maze of discontentment, searching for a way out but finding none. Pride sneaks in when we are uncertain about who we are in Christ, and when we don't believe what he says about us to be true. He says we are masterpieces; we were created on purpose and with a purpose. He says we were created to change the world for him.

Write down scriptures that describes how God sees you.

SILENCED BY PRIDE

Study - Reflect - Pray

WEEK SEVEN | DAY TWO

1. **Yesterday you wrote down scriptures that describe how God sees you. Re-read them now.**

2. **Do you believe what those scriptures say? Explain.**

When you are confident in the love God has for you it releases you from pride and comparison.

3. **Write down Genesis 1:27.**

Since you were made in the image of God why would you want to remake yourself in the image of someone else? It is enough to be made in the image of God; it is enough to be chosen by God!

4. **Write your prayer to God asking him to forgive you for allowing pride and comparison to take root in your life and thank him for making you in his image.**

SILENCING PRIDE

WEEK SEVEN | DAY THREE

"You made all the delicate, inner parts of my body and
knit me together in my mother's womb.
Thank you for making me so wonderfully complex!
Your workmanship is marvelous—how well I know it."
Psalm 139:13-14 NLT

The pride and comparison we have in our lives is destructive to not only our personal lives and relationship with Jesus but also to the church, Christ followers, the army.

Read Luke 10:38-42.

This story has a way of making us choose a side. Some of us are all about team Martha, because it makes sense that in a room full of men it would be her responsibility to take on the traditional and expected gender role of preparing the meal. I have a feeling that for Martha it was about more than the traditional role she was fulfilling; I think this was a pleasure for her. She was all about making everyone feel welcomed and comfortable. She wasn't preparing appetizers or desserts or a snack, the scriptures say she was preparing a big dinner. She was going above and beyond for Jesus and the other guests. This was what she was purposed to do and what she loved to do.

Others of us are thinking team Mary, totally team Mary! Because Mary wasn't restrained by tradition, she sat where the men sat. She didn't stand against the wall in the back, she didn't blend in with the crowd, and she didn't bow to tradition or society. Mary shirked her expected role and sat where she wanted to be–where she needed to be–at the feet of Jesus, not where she was expected to be.

This is today's conversation: in fact, there are theologies and whole denominations that have chosen the Mary or Martha team. There are those who think Martha, "the hostess with the mostest," behaved properly and honorably. Then there are those who believe Mary was just as much in her role and element as Martha was.

Do you find yourself wanting to take a side? Explain.

Pride will always make us lead people to the place we are, to the place that makes sense for us, to the place that doesn't push us out of our comfort zone. We will choose comfort for everyone around us, and we will choose each other's purpose based on what we are comfortable watching. We either want to push each other into the kitchen or out of the kitchen without any thought as to where God wants them, only to where we want them.

Most of the time we will choose the side we most identify with or are comfortable with. But why do we choose a team at all?

Why do we or you want Mary and Martha to be doing the same thing or living the same purpose? Explain.

Why do we or you think one is right over the other? Explain.

Pride. Pride in thinking we know better than anyone else. Pride in thinking we know better than God. Pride in thinking that everyone needs to stay in the lane we feel most comfortable with.

"It is the one and only Spirit who distributes all these gifts.
He alone decides which gift each person should have."
1 Corinthians 12:11 NLT

God created us on purpose, with the strengths we have, the purposes we have, the voices we have, and the abilities we have. He didn't make a mistake by making us different–it is a part of his perfect plan.

Read 1 Corinthians 12:4-6

It is our job to silence pride and accept God's plan as perfect and to trust that the calling he has placed on our lives is not a threat to each other's calling, but all are to serve God and to change the world for Jesus.

If Jesus were here today, I think his response to our need to push each other into traditional norms, positions, and titles would be the exact same response he gave to Martha. "My dear Martha, you are worried and upset over all these details! There is only one thing worth being concerned about. Mary has discovered it, and it will not be taken away from her."

What do you think "it" is? Explain.

I believe "it" is whatever God has purposed and called **you** to do, not me, not us but YOU!

The gifts, talents, purpose, and calling God has created each of us with is meant to change the world for Jesus, if we silence each other out of pride we are silencing the mission and mandate to change the world for Jesus, essentially, we are not silencing each other we are silencing the message of Jesus and we are silencing Jesus in our world.

We can learn a lesson from Martha. She wasn't happy with Mary and her decision to sit at the feet of Jesus. She wasn't content with scolding Mary later in private or trying to understand how important sitting at the feet of Jesus was to Mary. Martha was determined to have Mary corrected, and in the most public way, in front of their guests. She asked Jesus to correct, fix, scold, or rebuke her sister. Martha truly believed she was right in her request; she believed Mary needed to be put back on the right path, back in her rightful, traditional, and expected place.

I love that Jesus addresses Martha with so much kindness, patience, and love. He never corrected her for serving in her role as hostess, and he never corrected her for not sitting at his feet. His only response was to help her understand that Mary had found her place at the feet of Jesus, even if it wasn't the traditional role that Jesus, Martha, and Mary were accustomed to, and she was where she was purposed to be.

Write a prayer asking God to help you understand and accept the calling he has placed in the lives of the people around you and ask him to see the mission to change the world for Jesus as bigger than your pride.

SILENCING PRIDE

Study - Reflect - Pray

WEEK SEVEN | DAY FOUR

"There are different kinds of spiritual gifts, but the same Spirit is the source of them all.
There are different kinds of service, but we serve the same Lord.
God works in different ways, but it is the same God who does the work in all of us."
1 Corinthians 12:4-6 NLT

1. **Read Romans 12:6-13.**

2. **Do you believe other's purpose and calling diminishes yours? Explain.**

3. **How can you encourage the people in your life to not only embrace their purpose and calling but to change the world for Jesus with it? Explain.**

4. **Write a prayer to God with the struggle you may have with your calling or the calling of the people around you and ask him to show you the significance of each calling so you can live in harmony with others.**

SILENCED BY PRIDE

No Longer

WEEK SEVEN | DAY FIVE

"Live in harmony with each other.
Don't be too proud to enjoy the company of ordinary people.
And don't think you know it all!"
Romans 12:16 NLT

We are not victims of pride; we are volunteers to silence it!
The world will not be changed by conformity but by our differences.
The world will not be changed by complacency but by determination.
The world will not be changed by pride in ourselves but pride in God.

Write down Hebrews 10:24.

Let us think of ways to motivate one another to acts of love and good works.

Imagine an army consisting of God's daughters who silence pride and encourage each other to step courageously and boldly into their calling no matter what it is. Imagine a united army with the singular goal of changing the world for Jesus using the unique gifts, talents, purpose and calling that he created each of us with.

What would our world look like if we put the above into action? Explain.

God gave each of us different gifts so we can be specialists in that gift instead of having all the gifts but being stretched too thin trying to live them all out well. We don't have the time or the capacity to have all the gifts God needs us to have to change the world. "In his grace" he gave you the perfect gift, the gift that you and only you can live out well. "In his grace" he gifted each of us with the perfect gift, tailor made and woven into our being.

"In his grace, God has given us different gifts for doing certain things well.
So if God has given you the ability to prophesy,
speak out with as much faith as God has given you.
If your gift is serving others, serve them well.
If you are a teacher, teach well.
If your gift is to encourage others, be encouraging.
If it is giving, give generously.
If God has given you leadership ability, take the responsibility seriously.
and if you have a gift for showing kindness to others, do it gladly."
Romans 12:6-8 NLT

We silence pride by focusing on our own purpose while simultaneously cheering on our fellow Christ-followers on their journey to live out their gift and calling well.

Write down Philippians 2:3-4

This scripture doesn't say your life, purpose, or calling shouldn't be seen as important; it means we should see our life and purpose as part of God's greater plan, not that your plan needs to become God's plan. God is asking us to stay humble, know our place and purpose, and to help further his plan by partnering and encouraging others as they fulfill their purpose in whatever capacity God has called them to do it.

Are you willing to partner with and encourage others as they fulfill their purpose in whatever capacity God has called them to do it? Explain.

The impact your God-given purpose will make is far more important than worrying about how your purpose or the purpose of the people around you will impact you.

Your purpose may not be showcased on the world stage. It may not look good on social media, and it may not ever be seen by anyone other than you and the people who are changed because of it. However, that doesn't mean it is less than, less important, less impactful, or less inspiring. It means you have found "it" and "it" will never be taken from you. It means you are changing the world for Jesus. It means you are not a victim of pride but a volunteer to change it. You have a decision to make, you can be silenced by pride or you can silence pride, you can use your gifts and calling to change the world for Jesus or you can watch those who do.

What is your decision? Explain.

Below is a declaration to God and a warning to the enemy. If you want to join women around the world who have chosen to silence pride and change the world for Jesus then after reading your declaration sign your name with confidence.

> We, the Christian women of this world, no longer a silenced army. We are an army silencing pride. We are confident about who we are in Christ, and we believe what he says about us is true. We are masterpieces, created on purpose and with a purpose. We were created to change the world for Jesus. We are united in our cause of bringing unity and encouragement to each other, furthering God's plan and fulfilling it.
>
> We listen to each other, learn from each other, and grow together. We are not prideful, selfish, or self-centered. We no longer compare our lives or calling, and we no longer compete for importance. We cheer each other on, stand up for each other, and trust God's purpose and calling for each other's lives is good. We are a humble army, thinking of each other before ourselves and understanding that we are better and stronger together. We are ready to change the world for Jesus.

____

Signature

"Two people are better off than one, for they can help each other succeed."
Ecclesiastes 4:9 NLT

We are more than two: we are millions helping each other succeed in our mission to share Jesus with a lost and dying world.

When you choose to no longer be silenced by pride, but instead choose to stand in the face of it, you are not alone. God is standing right beside you. He stands next to you and says, "Now this is a girl I can change the world through."

____________________ **is a girl God can change the world through!**

SILENCED BY CULTURE

WEEK EIGHT | DAY ONE

We, the Christian women of this world, are a silenced army. Silenced by culture. A culture that says you are wrong. A culture that says God is wrong.

We cast our vote when we stay silent, and we give our approval with our lack of action. We are changing the world by remaining silent. We are making a difference by not making one at all.

Silenced by the pressures of this world. Silenced by the voice in our head. Silenced willingly. Silence is so much easier than opposing the loudest voices, the accusing voices and the debating voices. Silence is a way to keep the peace, keep our peace and let the world be changed not by our God but by the loudest voices that shape our culture.

Pressured to fit in.

Pressured to believe that wrong is right.

Pressured to accept lies as truth.

Pressured to believe that the message of Jesus breeds hate.

Pressured to water down our beliefs.

Pressured to hide our faith.

Pressured to believe God is wrong.

Pressured to bow to culture.

Pressured to stay silent.

Do you feel pressured to accept the lies above as truths? Explain.

Satan, the thief of our voice, the killer of our courage, and the destroyer of our faith has proven to be a worthy adversary. He has gathered his army, given them a voice, whispered lies, created a cause, and silenced his opposers.

We, the Christian women of the world, stay silent, seemingly unaffected by the battle, hiding in our homes and churches, ignoring the voice insulting our faith, our beliefs, and our God. We tell ourselves, *As long as it doesn't affect me, it's not my battle to fight.* We bury our heads in the sand waiting for the change we are supposed to bring. Waiting for someone else to fight our battle.

Do you believe the battle against the enemy needs you or do you believe it can be won without you? Explain.

Our enemy is not out to steal, kill, and destroy your way of life; he is out to destroy *God's way* of life, the life God planned and set in motion for us–along with the morals he put in place and the guardrails he set up. The enemy is out to destroy the purpose God created each one of us with. You have to know your enemy and his tactics to defeat him.

Write down 2 Corinthians 2:11.

Write down John 10:10.

When you accepted Jesus you volunteered for the army of Christ and agreed to fight for and uphold the Word of God. If our enemy can destroy God's way of life, our way of life will follow. If the world says divorce is okay, we believe them and we destroy our families with divorce. If illegal substances are made legal, we ignore the consequences and we silently watch as the people in our world become addicted. If abortions are legalized we deceive ourselves with the false assurance that it is right. The enemy is destroying God's way of life with the legalization of what culture says is right to them and for them.

Have you seen this in our world today? Explain.

Silently, we bow to culture. We compromise what we believe in the name of grace. We agree to sin to keep the peace, and we turn a blind eye to fit in. We take absolute truth and redefine it to fit our own desires. Finding it easier to bow than to stand, we are silenced. We conform to culture's distorted view of truth.

Have you ever compromised your Christ-centered beliefs to fit in? Explain.

"Don't copy the behavior and customs of this world,
but let God transform you
into a new person by changing the way you think..."
Romans 12:2a NLT

As women in the army of Christ, we don't get to interpret the Bible as we see fit; we don't get to pick and choose which parts we will follow and which ones we won't.

We have to fight the pressures to be convinced by culture to accept things as right that God says are wrong.

Have you ever accepted things as right that God says are wrong? Explain.

We don't get to contradict God. We don't define sin, God does. We don't get to rewrite the Bible to fit the culture around us. Anything that opposes or is in contradiction to the Word of God is a lie. Jesus says this about the enemy in John 8:44b (NLT): "When he lies, it is consistent with his character; for he is a liar and the father of lies." His lies have deceived us from the very beginning, starting with Eve, but it doesn't have to continue. We don't have to believe them, and we don't have to give in to them.

We are not victims of culture: We are volunteers to change it.

We were created on purpose and with a purpose. We were created to change the world for Jesus, not to hide from it. We are to be transformed to be like Jesus. To be like Jesus is to allow him to change the way we think, change the way we listen, and change the way we see the world around us. To be transformed by Jesus is to discern God's truths from Satan's lies. To be transformed is to see the world as God sees it–a world that needs Jesus.

Write a prayer asking God to show you what is God's truth and what is lies and to give you courage to accept what is God's truth and to live and uphold it.

SILENCED BY CULTURE

Study - Reflect - Pray

WEEK EIGHT | DAY TWO

1. **Write down Psalm 119:142**

"As I learn your righteous regulations,
I will thank you by living as I should!"
Psalm 119:7 NLT

2. **Do you struggle to accept things you know God says are wrong but you want to believe are right? Explain.**

"Make them holy by your truth; teach them your word, which is truth."
John 17:17 NLT

3. **Why do you struggle with your answer to question number two? Explain.**

4. **Write a prayer asking God to guide you through the struggles you listed in questions number two and three.**

SILENCING CULTURE

WEEK EIGHT | DAY THREE

We are living in a world where the culture is changing rapidly, it is changed by the loudest and most persistent voice. That voice is not different than the voice David heard from the giant, and the culture is not bigger than the giant David faced.

Read 1 Samuel Chapter 17.

There are three different stories playing out in the telling of this event, not unlike what we see in today's world. Goliath (the culture), the Israelite army (the women of the church - the silent army), and David (the women of the church - silent no longer).

Goliath, a giant in stature and in intimidation, and an opposer of Israel and their God. He taunted God's army: a silent army. He yelled insults at them with the arrogance of an unopposed bully. His message was "I defy the armies of Israel today!" What he really meant was, "I defy your God."

The Army of soldiers–ready and armed for battle, chosen and trained to defend and protect the people of God–was silenced by the size of the giant and the volume of his voice. An army brought down to a bow by words and threats; they were "terrified and deeply shaken." Their only defense for silence was a question: "Have you seen that giant?"

David, unmoved by discouragement or the size of the giant, bravely stands when the rest of the army bows. He boldly and courageously walked onto the battlefield, alone.

David wasn't concerned about the size of the giant; he knew the size of his God, and there was no comparison. He would not allow this giant to mock his God.

Today culture is the unopposed giant who hurls insults and taunts God's silent army, the church. Big, intimidating, loud, armed, battle-tested, unafraid, and repetitious in its insults to our God. It is unafraid to invite us into a battle, unafraid to mock our God, unafraid to challenge our beliefs, and unafraid to provoke us onto the battlefield.

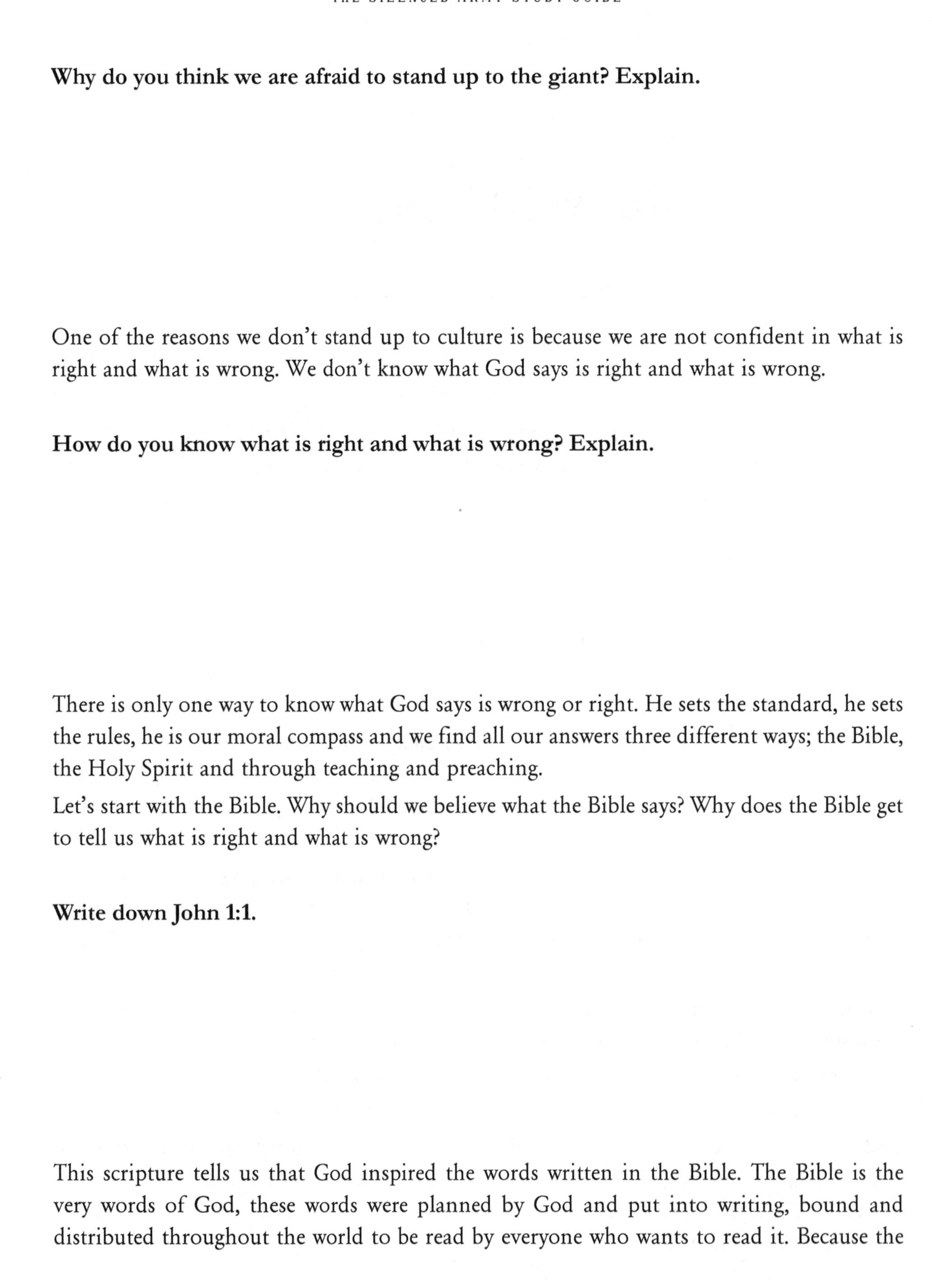

Why do you think we are afraid to stand up to the giant? Explain.

One of the reasons we don't stand up to culture is because we are not confident in what is right and what is wrong. We don't know what God says is right and what is wrong.

How do you know what is right and what is wrong? Explain.

There is only one way to know what God says is wrong or right. He sets the standard, he sets the rules, he is our moral compass and we find all our answers three different ways; the Bible, the Holy Spirit and through teaching and preaching.

Let's start with the Bible. Why should we believe what the Bible says? Why does the Bible get to tell us what is right and what is wrong?

Write down John 1:1.

This scripture tells us that God inspired the words written in the Bible. The Bible is the very words of God, these words were planned by God and put into writing, bound and distributed throughout the world to be read by everyone who wants to read it. Because the

Bible is filled with the words of God it can be trusted, believed and should be followed. It is the true manual to what is right and what is wrong.

"All Scripture is God-breathed and is useful for
teaching, rebuking, correcting and training in righteousness,"
2 Timothy 3:16 NIV

List the reasons the scriptures are useful, necessary, important and critical to our spiritual growth?

1.

2.

3.

4.

I love that the scripture says "useful." We don't have to read it, apply it or even obey it. BUT we don't get to rewrite it, argue it or change it to fit what we want to believe is right or wrong. The Holy Spirit is our second source of teaching you what God says is right and what is wrong.

"But you have received the Holy Spirit, and he lives within you,
so you don't need anyone to teach you what is true.
For the Spirit teaches you everything you need to know,
and what he teaches is true—it is not a lie.
So just as he has taught you, remain in fellowship with Christ."
1 John 2:27 NLT

What does the Spirit do?

What he teaches is__________ - it is not a_____________.

Write down John 14:26.

The Holy Spirit is to be trusted, believed, and listened to.

Pastors, Preachers, and Spiritual Leaders are the third source qualified to teach you what God says is right and what is wrong.

"He must hold firmly to the trustworthy message as it was taught,
so that by sound teaching he will be able to
encourage others and refute those who contradict this message."
Titus 1:9 BSB

Fill in the blanks below.

This scripture applies to every single one of us. We must ____________ to the

______________message as it was taught, so that by____________________

he will be able to __________________ and __________________ those who

_________________this message.

"Now these are the gifts Christ gave to the church:
the apostles, the prophets, the evangelists, and the pastors and teachers.
Their responsibility is to equip God's people to do his work
and build up the church, the body of Christ."
Ephesians 4:11-12 NLT

We, the Christian women of the world, have all the information, all the resources, and all the protection we need to stand up to the giant: to no longer be silenced by culture but to volunteer to silence the pressure to call right what God says is wrong.

Write down Romans 8:31.

David replied to the Philistine, *"You come to me with sword, spear, and javelin, but I come to you in the name of the LORD of Heaven's Armies—the God of the armies of Israel, whom you have defied." 1Samuel 17:45 NIV*

The giant is silenced.

SILENCING CULTURE

Study - Reflect - Pray

WEEK EIGHT | DAY FOUR

David, alone in his conviction and courage, was willing to stand up to the giant with no earthly guarantee that he would win. His victory was believing that God was on his side. His motivation was to defend his God, who will not be mocked. David stood on the battlefield, facing a giant and his army, and behind David there was an army unwilling to fight, silenced and bowing.

David leaned down to pick up his only earthly defense–five smooth stones. When he stood, he did not stand alone; he stood with God.

As he stood, this boy cast a God-sized shadow.

1. Do you feel alone in your stand against culture? Explain

"What, then, shall we say in response to these things?
If God is for us, who can be against us?"
Romans 8:31 NIV

2. **Does Romans 8:31 give you courage? Explain.**

3. **Write a prayer to God asking him to give you the same courage, confidence and boldness that David had.**

SILENCED BY CULTURE

No Longer

WEEK EIGHT | DAY FIVE

Christian women of the world, we will no longer be a silenced army. We will step onto the battlefield–not to fight with lost people but to fight *for* them. Our weapons meant to destroy the lies of culture and bring life to people. We fight with the message of Jesus, and this message will replace lies with truth, bring hope to the hopeless, healing to the sick and broken, joy to the depressed, peace to the anxious, direction to the lost, significance to the unseen, a hearing ear to the unheard, freedom to the enslaved and Heaven to the Hell-bound.

Write down John 3:17.

Too many people are caught in the grips of culture and are too afraid to leave for fear they will stand alone. They believe that to be a part of the world is to be a part of something big and greater than themselves. They so badly want to be a part of it and be accepted; they don't want to be set apart, rejected by culture, and hated. We can show them that there is freedom when you leave the throngs of people blindly following culture.

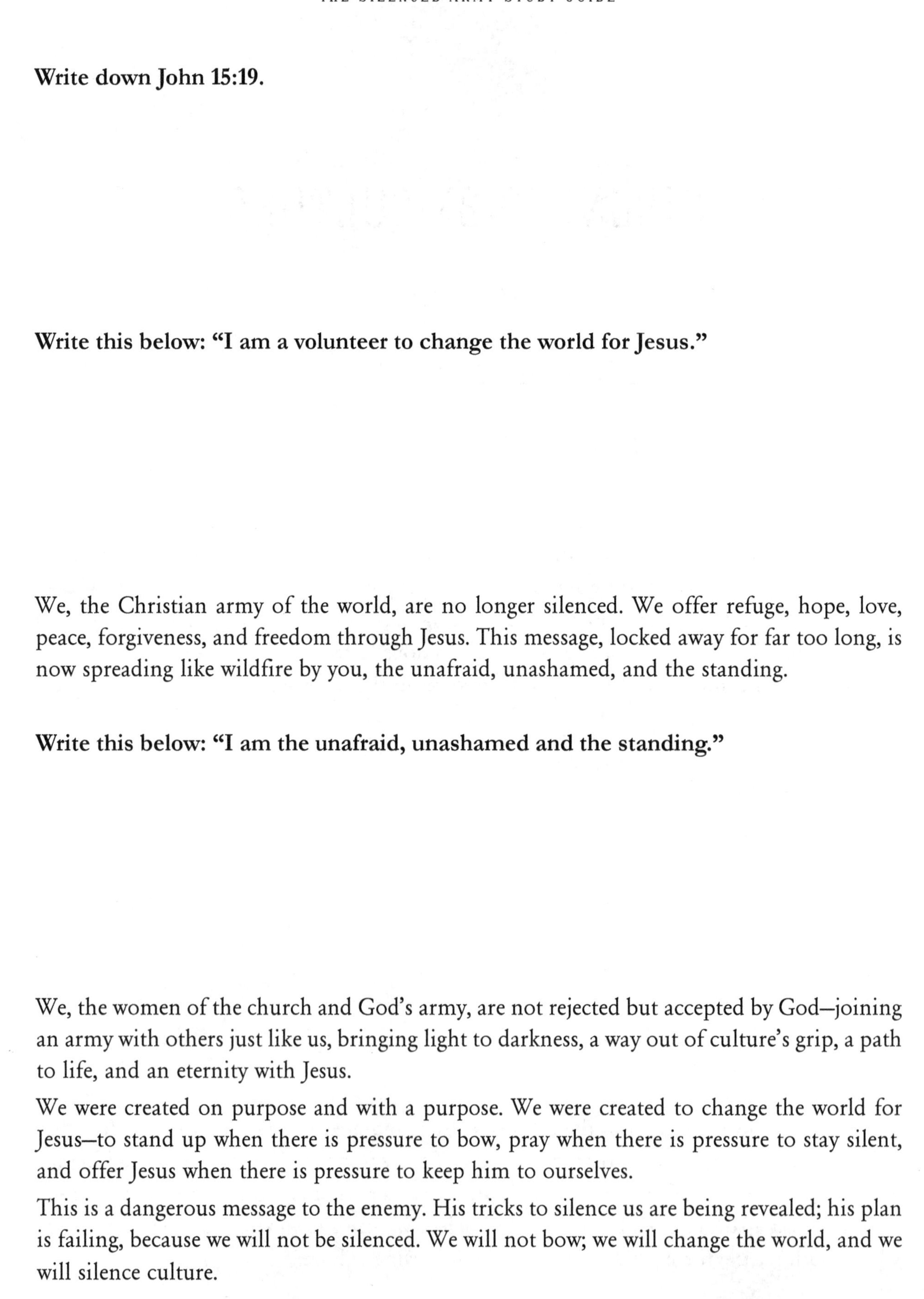

Write down John 15:19.

Write this below: "I am a volunteer to change the world for Jesus."

We, the Christian army of the world, are no longer silenced. We offer refuge, hope, love, peace, forgiveness, and freedom through Jesus. This message, locked away for far too long, is now spreading like wildfire by you, the unafraid, unashamed, and the standing.

Write this below: "I am the unafraid, unashamed and the standing."

We, the women of the church and God's army, are not rejected but accepted by God–joining an army with others just like us, bringing light to darkness, a way out of culture's grip, a path to life, and an eternity with Jesus.

We were created on purpose and with a purpose. We were created to change the world for Jesus–to stand up when there is pressure to bow, pray when there is pressure to stay silent, and offer Jesus when there is pressure to keep him to ourselves.

This is a dangerous message to the enemy. His tricks to silence us are being revealed; his plan is failing, because we will not be silenced. We will not bow; we will change the world, and we will silence culture.

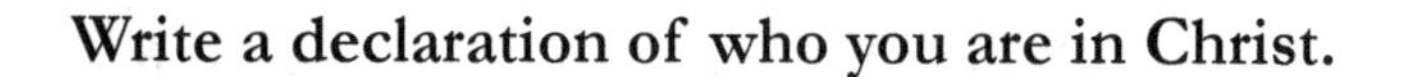

Write a declaration of who you are in Christ.

The battle is real, and it is raging around us. It is crucial to Satan's plan to silence every ONE of us, you are one, you are *the* one he wants to silence. He knows he isn't as effective as we are at discouraging each other, pulling each other down, demotivating each other, and silencing each other. He's hoping the silenced will bring the standing to a bow, because he needs every one of us to be silenced for his plan to work.

He only has to silence one of us to silence the rest, for if one of us speaks up, it gives courage to the rest.

Courage begins to grow when you realize you are not a victim of culture but rather a volunteer to change it. You are not stuck in the cultural muck, you are free to live, believe and share the freeing message of Jesus. You are free to change your world for Jesus.

Is there a culture in your life, home, family, friend group, relationship that you would like to see changed? Explain.

The battle is real, and you are needed in it. Every ONE of us is crucial to the plan God has. We must encourage each other, push each other, and motivate each other. We must sharpen each other. Every ONE–including you–the ONE is needed for God's plan to be fulfilled and for your world to be changed. The culture you listed above that needs to be changed is waiting on you to change it by inviting Jesus into it.

Write down 1Corinthians 16:13.

Women of Christ stand firm in your faith. Be courageous! Be strong!

Stand up unafraid to stand out.

Silence culture.

Unapologetically believe.

Stand up and say, wrong is wrong and right is right.

Believe truth over lies.

Boldly proclaim that the message of Jesus breeds love and not hate.

Be strong in my beliefs.

Be confident in my faith.

Believe God is right.

Bravely stand up to culture.

Be silent no longer.

Write "I will" in front of each of the above statements.

Jesus, the giver of your voice, the reason for your courage, and the foundation of your faith has proven to be a worthy Savior. He has gathered his army, given you a voice, and created a cause. He wants to change the world through you. It won't be easy; you won't always love the process of fulfilling your purpose and the calling on your life.

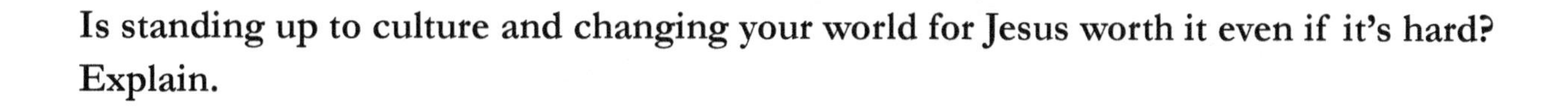

Is standing up to culture and changing your world for Jesus worth it even if it's hard? Explain.

The message of Jesus will not be embraced by everyone you tell, and you won't always be understood or accepted. However, our job is not to enforce the message of Jesus—our purpose is to share it. Emboldened by the God-sized shadow we cast, we don't back down, we don't give up, we don't silence our voice, and we don't bow.

"I have told you all this so that you may have peace in me.
Here on earth you will have many trials and sorrows.
<u>But take heart,</u>
<u>because I have overcome the world.</u>"
John 16:33 NLT

When you choose to no longer be silenced by culture, but instead choose to stand in the face of it, you are not alone. God is standing right beside you. He stands next to you and says, "Now this is a girl I can change the world through."

_______________________ is a girl God can change the world through!

SILENCED BY DISTRACTION

WEEK NINE | DAY ONE

We, the Christian women of this world, are a silenced army. Silenced by distraction. Distraction is a sly weapon used by the enemy. Distraction keeps us focused on good and bad things so we will miss the God things in our lives.

Distraction will keep us following whatever life throws at us, and distraction makes everything in our lives except God urgent. Distraction has a snowball effect, and if you open the door to it, distraction can take your whole life with it, one day at a time.

Are you easily distracted from what God wants to do in your life by the things in your life? Explain.

Distractions: keeping up, getting ahead, fitting in, chasing dreams, building a life, climbing the ladder, shattering ceilings, and holding on for dear life to everything you want over everything God wants for you and to do through you.

Write down 1 Corinthians 7:35.

We are not victims of distraction: We are volunteers. Distraction will hold our attention for as long as we are willing to let it. Distraction is a choice.

Christian women around the world are silenced by a life distracted away from God.

It is so easy to let life distract us because we can see the need for us in it. We tell ourselves: I am needed by my husband and kids, I am needed at work, I am needed by my family, and I am needed by my friends. What we miss is: I am needed by God.

What in your life do you let distract you from spending time with God and living out your purpose and calling? Explain.

We put our worth in the things that distract instead of things that last, because we think that the things that are distracting us need us. We delegate doing the things that last to someone else–someone more qualified, more important, or experienced. As long as it's someone else, anyone else. You are needed by God; you and your purpose are needed in this battle.

Do you choose distraction over doing God things that you perceive as hard? Explain.

Women, the army of God, no longer have the luxury of time to be distracted. We can no longer succumb to it or search for it. The world needs every single one of us focused, disciplined, and ready to change the world for Jesus. Our time on this earth is short, but our impact will last for generations. If we want to pass on hope past our lifetime, we will have to set aside the distractions of this world and put into focus the importance of living our lives on purpose.

"So, then, be careful how you live. Do not be unwise but wise, making the best use of your time because the times are evil."
Ephesians 5:15-16 ISV

"Make the best use of your time" means we have to take time seriously–it is finite while we are on this earth. Each minute that passes is a minute spent, a minute invested, or a minute wasted. We choose how to spend our time, and once spent, we can never get it back. Time can be full of purpose and impact or it can be wasted and squandered. What is the best use of your time? What gets all of your focus and attention? Are you living on purpose or chasing the distractions the enemy throws on your path? How you spend your time and your life pursuits is your choice, but distraction cannot dictate how you spend your life–it can only tempt you to follow it.

Write down Mark 4:19.

Distraction: the thief of focus, the thief of purpose and calling, and the thief of time.

To silence distraction, we must become intentional about how our time is spent, we do this by prioritizing what is in our lives, what requires our time, and what is a distraction.

Our lives can be put in three categories:

1. Urgent
2. Important
3. Fun

My "Urgent" list is full of the most precious things to me: God, time with God (studying the Bible and talking to God) husband, kids, work, purpose and calling.

What is on your Urgent list? List them below.

My "Important" list is full of, well, important things to me or important things that have to get done: family, friends, church, volunteering, grocery shopping, doctor or dentist appointments, etc. These things have to get done for our lives to function, so they are essential and important.

What is on your important list? List them below.

My "Fun" list is the best: vacations, spending time with friends, going for walks, playing board games, going to the beach, DISNEY WORLD (I would love for this to be on my Urgent list!), watching old movies and taking a much needed bath.

What is on your fun list? List them below.

Prioritize your life so your life won't take priority!

Our lives are full, fun, busy, crazy, hectic, and can be all-consuming. However, we can't let these things control us.

You have to take control of your life and choose what is important based on your values and beliefs, based on what is important to you, and most importantly, what is important to God. Your life is a gift from God—every minute, day, year, and decade is precious. He filled it with every good thing you have. But when your good things become your only things and God becomes an unwelcome distraction in your life, then the life you were blessed with stops being blessed, and you become a slave to it.

Below write a prayer to God asking him to help you see the things he wants you to do as urgent and not something to be distracted from.

SILENCED BY DISTRACTION

Study - Reflect - Pray

WEEK NINE | DAY TWO

"Keep your eyes straight ahead; ignore all sideshow distractions."
Proverbs 4:25 MSG

1. **What is the best use of your time? Explain.**

2. **What gets all of your focus and attention? Explain.**

3. Are you living on purpose or chasing the distractions the enemy throws on your path? Explain.

4. Below write a prayer to God telling him about your struggle with distraction.

SILENCING DISTRACTION

WEEK NINE | DAY THREE

"But all too quickly the message is crowded out by the worries of this life,
the lure of wealth, and the desire for other things,
so no fruit is produced."
Mark 4:19 NLT

In 1 Samuel, we read about the first king of Israel, named Saul. He didn't start out as king, but he was hand-picked by God to become king. The prophet Samuel told Saul about the decision God made, but from the very beginning, Saul wasn't convinced. Saul didn't think he was good enough. He didn't trust God's plan, and he was distracted by insecurity.

Distraction doesn't always come from the things we hear, see, and do, nor from family, career and responsibilities. More often than not the distractions that silence us come from our thoughts and feelings.

Do you allow feelings of insecurity or insignificance to silence you?

Do you feel unprepared, unqualified or uneducated when it comes to the purpose and calling God has called you to fulfill?

"'I am here to tell you that you and your family are the focus of all Israel's hopes.'
Saul replied, 'But I'm only from the tribe of Benjamin, the smallest tribe in Israel,
and my family is the least important of all the families of that tribe!
Why are you talking like this to me?'"
1 Samuel 9:20b-21 NLT

Saul, the appointed king of Israel, never got past his feeling of unworthiness. He never grasped the importance of his purpose and calling, and because of that, he never took it seriously. He never understood that the thoughts he had about himself were a distraction from his calling. He lived his life making up his own rules, following God's instructions halfheartedly, and trying to please others. He allowed himself to be distracted, because he didn't know just how important he was to God.

"And Samuel told him,
'Although you may think little of yourself,
are you not the leader of the tribes of Israel?
The LORD has anointed you king of Israel.
And the LORD sent you on a mission…'"
1 Samuel 15:17-18a NLT

"Although you may think little of yourself." Samuel called out Saul's insecurity and his distraction, and then followed up with a question: "Are you not the leader of the tribes of Israel?" I don't believe Samuel was looking for an answer; he was leading Saul to the answer and reminding him of his calling and purpose. Samuel goes on to say, "The Lord has anointed you...the Lord sent you on a mission."

Insert your name in the blank.

____________________ although you may think little about yourself you are called to change the world for Jesus using the gifts, talents, purpose and calling God created you with.

We are anointed and appointed to change the world for Jesus. We have been sent on a mission and have been commissioned and positioned to live out the purpose God has infused inside each of us. Distraction, feelings of unworthiness, or being unqualified are no excuse for disobedience.

Christian women of this world–God's army–although you may think little of yourselves, have you not been anointed and appointed to change the world for Jesus?

Write down John 15:16.

When we don't know how important our purpose is and how critical it is to live it out, we allow ourselves to be distracted, we allow ourselves to be silenced, and we allow distraction to bring us down to a bow. We were created on purpose and with a purpose. We were created to change the world for Jesus. This must be on our Urgent list. This must be a priority. This must be our mission. This is not a sacrifice, even though sometimes it may feel like it; this is a privilege. It is a privilege to be chosen by God to change the world for him, and it is an honor to tell his story.

Does putting God's calling for you life on your Urgent list feel like a sacrifice to you? Explain.

Saul thought he was sacrificing everything by becoming king. He thought he was doing the right thing and felt his plans were right because they were right to him. His intentions were good, but his intentions were not God's plans or commands. Saul wanted to please God with his sacrifice, but God never asked him for that. He asked him for obedience and submission.

"But Samuel replied,
'What is more pleasing to the LORD:
your burnt offerings and sacrifices
or your obedience to his voice?
Listen! Obedience is better than sacrifice
and submission is better than offering…'"
1 Samuel 15:22a NLT

When God wants you to sacrifice, he will tell you. Until then, he wants your obedience, he wants your submission, and he wants to be first on your Urgent list.

Your purpose is way too important to be distracted by everyday life. You were created to change the world, not to be changed by your world. Our responsibility is to bring Jesus into our lives not allow our lives to kick Jesus out of it.

How many times have you chosen to allow something on your Fun list take up time that was supposed to be spent with Jesus? Explain.

We need to silence distraction so we can give voice to our purpose and calling. The enemy loves it when we stay distracted with the things God has blessed us with. We must put God first, every time, all the time, and without fail.

Write a prayer asking God to forgive you for all the times you have allowed distraction to silence you and pull you away from what God has asked you to do.

SILENCING DISTRACTION

Study - Reflect - Pray

WEEK NINE | DAY FOUR

On day one of this week's study you put your priorities into three categories: Urgent, Important and Fun. These things are what your life consist of, it is what you spend your minutes, days, weeks, months and years doing. All this time adds up to a lifetime and if you are not intentional about your life you can easily come to the end having spent the whole of it silenced by distraction.
You prioritized what is important to you and now that you know you need to prioritize changing the world for Jesus using the gifts, talents, purpose and calling he gave you, it is time to list your priorities again, this time put God first in every category.

"So, then, be careful how you live. Do not be unwise but wise, making the best use of your time because the times are evil."
Ephesians 5:15-16 ISV

List the gifts, talents, purpose or calling you know you need to use to change the world for Jesus and then how and when you will use them.

1. **Urgent**

2. **Important**

3. **Fun**

SILENCED BY DISTRACTION

No Longer

WEEK NINE | DAY FIVE

We, the Christian women of the world, need to silence distraction and give voice to intentionality. We need to be focused and determined to change the world for Jesus.

Daily time spent in conversation with God will keep us focused on what is urgent. Daily time spent getting to know his character and his love for us through reading the Bible will show us what is important. Being obedient to what he has purposed us to do will be fun—not just fun—but a blast and the ride of a lifetime as well as a purpose and calling fulfilled. I know from experience that you will never regret choosing obedience over distraction. Never! Look straight ahead, and fix your eyes on what lies before you.

Write down Proverbs 4:26-27.

"Mark out a straight path for your feet;
stay on the safe path; Don't get sidetracked;
keep your feet from following evil."
Proverbs 4:26-27 NLT

Jesus is the hope of the world, and we are his messengers. We deliver the good news of Jesus, tell of forgiveness and hope, and model freedom in Christ. We cannot be distracted; we have to be focused on finding every possible way to share Jesus. We have to make the best use of our time, and we have to believe that God has chosen us and appointed us to change the world for him.

When you are focused and intentional do you accomplish more? Explain.

"Some men came carrying a paralyzed man on a sleeping mat.
They tried to take him inside to Jesus, but they couldn't reach him because of the crowd.
So, they went up to the roof and took off some tiles. Then they lowered the sick man on his mat
down into the crowd, right in front of Jesus. Seeing their faith, Jesus said to the man,
'Young man, your sins are forgiven…' 'Stand up, pick up your mat, and go home!'"
Luke 5:18-20,24b NLT

The men carrying the paralyzed man were not distracted from their goal of getting their friend to Jesus. When their path was blocked, they climbed up to the roof. If there was a problem, they were going to find a solution. Can you imagine how hard that was? I struggle to get on the roof carrying only my own weight and using a ladder. They were carrying a paralyzed man who couldn't help them at all. But that didn't stop them; they were focused on their mission.

After what I am sure was an exhausting trek to the top of the house, they had to pull up the roofing, make a hole big enough for a man to fit through, and make a way to Jesus. They had to be determined, focused, and free of distractions.

When you are focused, creativity has room to bloom, and these men were focused. Their friend's healing depended on it.

The young man would never have made it to the feet of Jesus and he never would have been forgiven of his sins and healed if it wasn't for "some men" who were focused, determined, creative, and cared enough about this man to put his life on their Urgent list.

This is a beautiful example of love for the lost and those in need of healing. They modeled how focused we should be in bringing people to Jesus: no distraction, no distracting, just pure faith in Jesus and love for everyone he loves.

Can you image what our world would look like today if we were just as focused at bringing people to Jesus as these men? Explain.

How would the lives of the people you know be changed if you were focused on bringing them to Jesus? Explain.

My favorite part of the story is these three words, "seeing their faith." He wasn't just talking about the paralyzed young man. He was talking about all of them. Jesus saw the faith of the men who wouldn't be stopped until their friend was healed, and he was moved. Their faith motivated them to act on behalf of a man who couldn't do it for himself. Jesus saw himself in those men; he saw his love shining through them, and he saw men who knew the difference one encounter with Jesus can make.

Do you want Jesus to see himself in you? Explain.

Do you want to be the woman who is focused on bringing the hurting, broken, abused, addicted, enslaved, forgotten, unseen, unheard and lost to Jesus? Explain.

You are purposed to bring people to the feet of Jesus, you are purposed to carry Jesus to people who can't make it to him on their own. They need your faith, your determination, and your do-whatever-it-takes attitude. The battle needs you!

Here we are at a declaration moment, one that can change your life and the world around you. If you are ready to silence distraction and commit to being intentional with your time, gifts, talents, purpose and calling then declare the statement below and then sign your name as a commitment to God and a threat to the enemy.

> We, the Christian women of the world, choose to silence distraction and embrace the purpose and calling God has given us. We choose to see our calling not as a sacrifice but as obedience and submission. We choose to bring people to Jesus and not be discouraged or distracted, but courageous and focused. We will find a way, even when it looks like there is no way to bring people to the feet of Jesus. We choose to change the world for Jesus.

____

Signature

When you choose to no longer be silenced by distraction but instead choose to stand in the face of it, you are not alone. God is standing right beside you. He stands next to you and says, "Now this is a girl I can change the world through."

____________________ **is a girl God can change the world through!**

THE ARMY

WEEK TEN | DAY ONE

This final week is about declaring who we are in Christ and what we are committing to do for him. We are wise to the enemy's tactics and will no longer be deceived, tricked, used, or silenced. We are honored that God chose us to take the message of Jesus into a hurting and broken world. We are honored to change the world for Jesus.
We, the Christian women of the world–half of God's army–SILENCED NO LONGER.

Below write these words; "I will be silenced no longer."

We are not victims of this sinful world but rather volunteers to change it. We are volunteers in the army of Christ.

We were created resilient, strong, caring, compassionate, loving, hopeful, courageous, skilled, intelligent, creative, and passionate, to name a few.

Write down Isaiah 40:31.

We are risk takers, heart menders, advice givers, faith builders, world changers, and history makers.

Not one of us are all these things, but each of us are some of these things, and together we are an army. We are a volunteer army. We are women created by God on purpose and for a purpose. We were created to change the world around us for Jesus.

We are women no longer silenced by fear, pain, doubt, unforgiveness, shame, offense, pride, culture, and distraction. Half of God's army standing up, bravely joining the fight– aware that the battle being fought requires all of us to make a stand using our purpose, calling, actions, and voice to bring Jesus into our world again.

We live in a time where women are no longer afraid to stand up for our beliefs and fight for the right to choose the life God has laid out for us.

What are you no longer silenced by? List them below.

Women are making progress. We are changing the world. We are making a difference.

Women of God are no longer afraid or ashamed to stand up to culture, no longer ashamed or afraid to stand up for Jesus, share Jesus, follow Jesus as he leads us, step into our purpose and calling, and encourage each other to live out our purpose. We are no longer focused on ourselves, but on a lost and broken world. A world that needs Jesus! A world that needs our God-given purpose. No longer silent, but ready and willing to share Jesus with everyone we cross paths with: the lost, strayed, injured, weak, broken, enslaved, forgotten, abused, neglected, unseen, unheard and defenseless.

Are you ready to give the time, gifts, talents, purpose and calling away to the world so we can change the world for Jesus? Explain.

We, the Christian women of the world, are willing to pull over, stop in our tracks, make time for the lost, and run to the hurting. We vow to take every opportunity to share Jesus with a world on the edge of death. With eyes wide open, we look for people who need Jesus. We will be the generation that speaks up and stands up for a world that is out of control and on the brink of destruction. We have an internal alarm that God has put in our hearts: The alarm is sounding and beeping to the beat of eternity. For too long we have silenced this alarm—for too long we have ignored it. Now is the time, we feel its urgency humming in us and around us. We are waking up; we are standing up and fulfilling our purpose and calling for this time and for this generation.

Write down Ecclesiastes 3:11

Fill your name in the blanks.

____________________ mission isn't to save anyone: it is to introduce them to the One who will.

____________________ mission isn't to convince anyone: it is to introduce them to the Truth.

____________________ mission isn't to heal anyone: it is to bring them to the Healer.

____________________ mission isn't to fight with anyone: it is to fight for them.

All of us are messengers in his army, sharing the message of Jesus, speaking the truth in love, and letting God do the rest. Our heart breaks for what his heart breaks for, as we search just as he does for the lost, strayed, injured, and weak, we vow to share Jesus with them the way Jesus has shown himself to us.

Write down Ezekiel 34:16.

Jesus searches for the lost, strayed, injured, and weak and brings them to us or brings us to them. Silent no more, we use our voice to bring healing, hope, salvation, restoration and... JESUS.

Day and night, generation after generation, he seeks out his lost kids, willing and wanting to make them whole. Day and night, generation after generation, he is raising his army to go out into all the world and share the good news of Jesus. Generation after generation, he searches the world for the willing and ready, for his army. He has found the willing generation, right now–**it is us**!

Are you willing to be part of the generation that teaches the next generation how to love like Jesus does? In what way can you start today?

We are making progress. We are changing the world. We are making a difference.

Write down Matthew 28:19-20.

You can be sure of this, you are never alone in your mission to change the world for Jesus, he is with you even to the end of the age.

"I pray that from his glorious, unlimited resources
he will empower you with inner strength through his Spirit."
Ephesians 3:16 NLT

THE ARMY

Study - Reflect - Pray

WEEK TEN | DAY TWO

Your willingness is all God needs. David was a shepherd boy, Moses was a fugitive, Noah built a boat for flooding when he had never seen rain, Esther was an orphan taken in by her uncle, Joseph was thrown into a pit and then sold, Mary was a young girl, Paul persecuted Christians, and Peter, James and John were fishermen. Their only common qualification to be chosen to change the world for Jesus was their "yes." God did the rest.

1. Write down Isaiah 40:29.

2. Write down Philippians 4:13.

3. Fill in the blanks.

I can ____________________ because my strength comes from God.

I can ____________________ because my strength comes from God.

I can ____________________ because my strength comes from God.

I can ____________________ because my strength comes from God.

Look up and write down a scripture that speaks courage, boldness and stamina to change your world for Jesus.

THE ARMY - RELEASED

WEEK TEN | DAY THREE

"A final word: Be strong in the Lord and in his mighty power."
Ephesians 6:10 NLT

The past nine weeks have been hard, challenging, and exciting. You have learned what has silenced you and what it will take to silence those challenges so you can change not only your world but so together we can change the whole world for Jesus. Today we will identify a few culture driven agendas that need to have God's truths bravely, courageously and consistently spoken into them.
We are making progress. We are changing the world. We are making a difference.

"Children are a gift from the LORD; they are a reward from him."
Psalm 127:3 NLT

Write down Psalm 139:16.

God gives us the right to stand up for the unborn. We have the right to introduce women to Jesus' grace and forgiveness. We are obligated to share with women around the world that they are not alone. They have a choice, and they and their unborn baby matter to God. They were created on purpose and with a purpose and that life planned or unplanned by humans are created and planned by God.

We are making progress. We are changing the world. We are making a difference.

"Direct your children onto the right path, and when they are older, they will not leave it."
Proverbs 22:6 NLT

Write down Deuteronomy 6:6-7.

God gives us the right and mandate to speak up in our homes and in every school around the world about our relationship with Jesus and our Christian beliefs. We have to pray and share the hope and healing we have found in Jesus with a generation that is killing themselves over bullying, depression, loneliness, anxiety, and rejection. We get to teach our kids to stand up for Jesus–to not be afraid or ashamed but to stand up and silence culture, fear, doubt, and pressure.

We are making progress. We are changing the world. We are making a difference.

Read Mark 10:6-9 and 1 Corinthians 6:9.

Write down Matthew 19:4.

God gives us the right to share the truth about love, relationships and marriage. The truth that no relationship will ever be fulfilling unless Jesus is in it. We can't marry whomever we want or be whatever gender we want to be; we don't get to throw God's workmanship and masterpiece out the window and believe that we know better than him. We have the right to speak the truth–God's truth–without judgment or shame.

We are making progress. We are changing the world. We are making a difference.

Write down Luke 14:18-19.

God gives us the right and mandate to stand up for the abused, trafficked, sold, forgotten, unseen, unheard, persecuted, and discarded by the world. Women, the Army of God, standing up for our sisters, arms linked around the world, encircling the vulnerable and sharing the Healer of all wounds with them.

The world will tell us, "You are making progress. You are changing the world. You are making a difference." The world will be right!

"And they have conquered him by the blood of the Lamb
and by the word of their testimony,
for they loved not their lives even unto death."
Revelation 12:11 ESV

Write down 2 Corinthians 4:1-2.

We shape the world with the sound of our voice. We cast our vote when we speak up, and we stand up by taking action. No longer silent, we are changing the world, and we are making a difference.

Why are you silencing the enemies voice in your life? Explain.

Who are you silencing the enemies voice in your life for? Explain.

Are you confident that one encounter with Jesus can change the life of the person you are sharing him with? Explain.

We boldly take these steps, and so many others, because we know why we do it, we know who we are doing it for, and we are confident in the difference one encounter with Jesus can make.

WE ARE NOT VICTIMS OF THIS SINFUL WORLD.
WE ARE VOLUNTEERS TO CHANGE IT.

Jesus: the first volunteer, the first to make a stand, and the first to change our world.

Jesus stood on the cross, arms outstretched, welcoming our sin, fear, doubt, unforgiveness, shame, brokenness, rebellion, and silence. On that cross, he stood up for us, he stood up with us, and he stood up to our accusers. He did it without hesitation, and he did it with love and compassion for us, knowing that his sacrifice would render us free. We are free from an eternity in Hell, free from the bondage of culture, free from shame, free from pain, and free to change the world for him, using the purpose and calling that he created us with.

"Because of the joy awaiting him, he endured the cross,
disregarding its shame.
Now he is seated in the place of honor beside God's throne."
Hebrews 12:2b NLT

If Jesus didn't feel shame, neither should we! Neither should we!

We will not be ashamed. We will not be silent, because we know that the next generation is watching and waiting to see what legacy we will leave for them. We will not be ashamed, because we know people need Jesus and culture needs to be changed. Fear, pain, doubt, unforgiveness, shame, offense, pride, culture, and distraction will gladly be brought to a bow before Jesus.

Write a prayer of thanksgiving to God for freeing you from the grips of silence and releasing you to boldly change the world for Jesus.

THE ARMY

Study - Reflect - Pray

WEEK TEN | DAY FOUR

Yesterday we identified a few culture-driven agendas that need to have God's truths bravely, courageously, and consistently spoken into them. Those are world-wide problems that will take an army–God's Army–to come together with one united voice to silence those lies with God's truth.

Those are not the only problems in our world, I know God has shown you problems in your community, friend circle, family, workplace, state, country or world that need the voice of Jesus infused into it.

He showed you this problem because he wants you to become part of the solution, if he showed you the problem then he will give you the solution on how to bring Jesus into it.

1. **What problem, issue or need has he shown you and given you a passion for? Explain.**

2. **How can you be a part of the solution? Explain.**

3. **What is keeping you from starting or joining the cause against this problem? Explain.**

4. **What is the solution to the problem stated above? Explain.**

5. **Whatever your concerns, fears, worries, anxieties or hesitations are, write them in a prayer to God below.**

THE ARMY

Silent No Longer

WEEK TEN | DAY FIVE

"A final word: Be strong in the Lord and in his mighty power."
Ephesians 6:10 NLT

Congratulations! You are on the last day of a ten-week intense battle of identifying the things that silence you. You bravely, courageously, and boldly stood up to these things and with God on your side and fighting with you, you are now silencing them.

We know the difference God has made in our lives and we know how the enemy has stolen our voice with lies and tactics that we are now wise to. We are on a mission to no longer be silenced but to use our voice to change the world for Jesus.

The world will notice and will tell us "You are making progress. You are changing the world. You are making a difference." The world will be right!

We shape the world with the sound of our voice. We cast our vote when we speak up, and we stand up by taking action. No longer silent, we are changing the world, and we are making a difference.

Write down Matthew 5:14.

Today is the day you look for opportunities to share Jesus with your world: your husband, your kids, your family, your friends, your neighbors, your co-workers, and anyone who will listen.

List the people you will pray for and look for the opportunity to share Jesus with them.

Today is the day you start!

When should you start?

There is no wrong time to share Jesus with the people around you, and there is no gesture too small, no circumstance too big. Eternity hangs in the balance. Now is the time! Now is the time to stand!

Go into the world ready to share the good news with everyone!

"And then he told them,
'Go into all the world and preach the Good News to everyone.
Anyone who believes and is baptized will be saved.
But anyone who refuses to believe will be condemned.'"
Mark 16:15-16 NLT

"Therefore, go and make disciples of all the nations,
baptizing them in the name of the Father and the Son and the Holy Spirit.
Teach these new disciples to obey all the commands I have given you.
And be sure of this:
I am with you always, even to the end of the age."
Matthew 28:19-20 NLT

"And be sure of this: I am with you always, even to the end of the age."

We are living in a world that is used to taking the voice God gave them and using it against him. We are used to hearing wrong called right, used to being shamed for our beliefs, used to compromising our faith, and used to being silent. Silenced with marches, chants, and bobbing signs, we were intimidated; we accepted defeat, and we silently bowed.

NO LONGER! We are the Christian women of the world. We are God's army and this is our declaration! Let it sink into your heart and soul, let it fuel you, motivate you and fill you with determination. Women around the world will be reading this same declaration, you will not be alone in this battle and you will not be standing alone, we are one, standing under the banner of our Savior.

Read the below declaration out loud.

> We are the generation who will no longer be silenced, and we will not pass a silenced voice to the next generation. We will not be fearful, doubtful, unforgiving, shamed, offended, prideful, distracted, or bullied by culture.

NO! We will be a beacon of hope, a light in the darkness, the voice of truth, the helping hand and crying shoulder, the uncompromised in our faith, the courageous in the sharing of Jesus, the prayer warrior, the Bible reader, the church attender, the generous giver, the leader, teacher and preacher, and the ones who stand when the rest of the world bows.

We are making progress. We are changing the world. We are making a difference.

We are an army united by God himself. We are an army with the common goal of sharing Jesus with the world. We are an army who wants the next generation to carry the message of Jesus forward. We are an army who wants to stop and drown out the voice of the enemy with the message and righteousness of Jesus.

Did you feel the courage, excitement and determination rise up inside of you? Explain.

We will make a difference; God is counting on us. He's calling us to unite, to link arms in our Christ-centered beliefs, to defeat and overwhelm the enemy's message with the message of Jesus, and to stand with confidence and courage. He is calling us to speak as one voice and march as one army.

We are God's army; we fight for and with him, and we are accompanied and led by him.

And you can be sure of this: he is with us until our end and the end. He is the creator and the finisher of all things both on earth and in Heaven. He is the creator and finisher of all purpose and calling both in you and lived through you, even to the end. Don't give up, don't give in, and resolve to never be silent.

When you choose to no longer be silenced but instead choose to stand, you are not alone. God is standing right beside you. He stands next to you and says,

"Now this is a girl I can change the world through!"

Women: the army of God. Created on purpose and with a purpose. Created to change the world around us for Jesus.

________________________ is a girl God can change the world through!

CPSIA information can be obtained
at www.ICGtesting.com
Printed in the USA
LVHW061505030721
691839LV00012B/956